The Param Vir Chakra is the most important military award in India. Since its institution on 26 January, 1950, it has been awarded to 21 bravehearts of the Indian Armed Forces.

To be considered worthy of this honour, a warrior needs to display the utmost courage in the field of battle. Whether on land, at sea, or in the air, he must display the willingness to sacrifice all when faced by the enemy.

PARAM VIR CHAKRA

THE ULTIMATE HONOUR

Contents

Contents

Story and Research: Vaneeta Vaid
Colourists: C. Ramesh, Prakash S., Silambarasan K.,
Raghavendra Kamath, Ritoparna Hazra, Adarsh Achari
Layout: Sivajith S., Aparna Kapur
Cover: Arijit Dutta Chowdhury, Ghanshyam Bochgeri
Art Director: Savio Mascarenhas

Editor: Reena Ittyerah Puri

MAJOR SOMNATH SHARMA

THERE HAS NEVER BEEN A LACK OF PATRIOTS IN OUR COUNTRY. THE INDIAN ARMED FORCES ARE FILLED WITH STIRRING STORIES OF COURAGEOUS MEN, WHO DISPLAYED UNQUESTIONING LOYALTY TO THE NATION. OUR FIRST STORY IS OF ONE SUCH INDIVIDUAL AND IT BEGINS IN THE EARLY 1930S WITH LITTLE SOM.

I ALSO WANT TO JOIN THE ARMY, PAPA.

HA HA! I THINK YOU SHOULD STUDY FOR THE I.C.S.* AND JOIN THE GOVERNMENT, SOM. THAT IS A MUCH BETTER JOB.

NO! ALL I WANT IS TO JOIN THE INDIAN ARMY.

SOMNATH WAS FROM A FAMILY OF ARMY OFFICERS. HIS FATHER, AMAR NATH SHARMA, WENT ON TO BECOME A GENERAL IN THE ARMY.

*INDIAN CIVIL SERVICES

AT THE AGE OF TEN, SOMNATH'S PARENTS TOOK HIM TO MEET MAJOR GENERAL BRUCE HEY, THE DISTRICT COMMANDER OF LUCKNOW.

I HOPE I GET ADMISSION.

SOMNATH WAS HOPING TO GET INTO THE PRINCE OF WALES MILITARY COLLEGE^ IN DEHRADUN.

^PRINCE OF WALES MILITARY COLLEGE WAS LATER RENAMED RASHTRIYA INDIAN MILITARY COLLEGE (R.I.M.C.).

SOMNATH'S CONFIDENCE IMPRESSED THE MAJOR GENERAL AND HE WAS INDUCTED INTO THE MILITARY COLLEGE IMMEDIATELY.

HIS ARMY TRAINING BEGAN AT THE AGE OF TEN!

AFTER R.I.M.C., SOMNATH JOINED THE INDIAN MILITARY ACADEMY. HE PASSED OUT OF I.M.A. IN 1942.

HE WAS A COMMISSIONED OFFICER AT THE AGE OF 19!

DURING THE BURMA* CAMPAIGN IN WORLD WAR II –

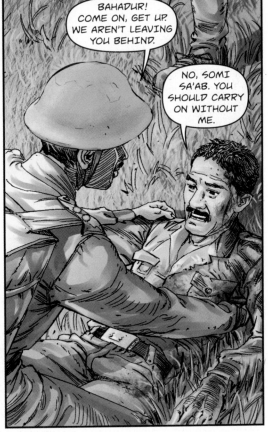

BAHADUR! COME ON, GET UP. WE AREN'T LEAVING YOU BEHIND.

NO, SOMI SA'AB. YOU SHOULD CARRY ON WITHOUT ME.

*BURMA IS NOW MYANMAR.

TAKE THAT MAN OFF YOUR SHOULDER RIGHT NOW! YOU CANNOT AFFORD TO SLOW DOWN.

WITH ALL DUE RESPECT, SIR, THIS SOLDIER HAS LOST A LOT OF BLOOD. HE CANNOT WALK ON HIS OWN.

SOMNATH RAN BACK TO HIS CAMP AS FAST AS HE COULD.

I DON'T KNOW HOW I CAN THANK YOU, SOMI SA'AB.

GET BETTER SOON, BAHADUR. YOU NEED YOUR REST.

BAHADUR SURVIVED TO TELL THE TALE!

ON 31 OCTOBER, 1947 –

IS IT NECESSARY FOR YOU TO GO TO KASHMIR ON SUCH A DANGEROUS MISSION WITH A HOCKEY INJURY?

YOU KNOW I HAVE TO, MA.

YOU SHOULD BE CAREFUL, SOM! DO YOU REALISE HOW MUCH ALL THIS WORRIES ME?

YOU ARE THE WIFE AND THE MOTHER OF ARMY MEN.

YOU SHOULD BE PROUD OF US.

I AM MORE THAN PROUD. BUT I AM ALSO A MOTHER AND I WORRY.

I'M NOT AFRAID. THE BULLE WITH MY NAME ON IS ALREADY OUT THE NOTHING CAN STOP TILL THEN, I SHALL L FEARLESSLY! I WILL BACK BEFORE YOU KNOW IT!

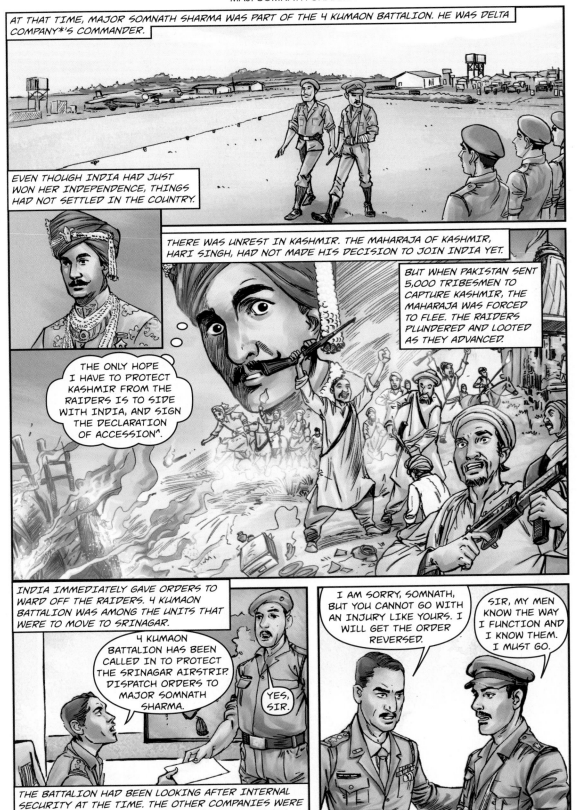

AT THAT TIME, MAJOR SOMNATH SHARMA WAS PART OF THE 4 KUMAON BATTALION. HE WAS DELTA COMPANY*'S COMMANDER.

EVEN THOUGH INDIA HAD JUST WON HER INDEPENDENCE, THINGS HAD NOT SETTLED IN THE COUNTRY.

THERE WAS UNREST IN KASHMIR. THE MAHARAJA OF KASHMIR, HARI SINGH, HAD NOT MADE HIS DECISION TO JOIN INDIA YET.

BUT WHEN PAKISTAN SENT 5,000 TRIBESMEN TO CAPTURE KASHMIR, THE MAHARAJA WAS FORCED TO FLEE. THE RAIDERS PLUNDERED AND LOOTED AS THEY ADVANCED.

THE ONLY HOPE I HAVE TO PROTECT KASHMIR FROM THE RAIDERS IS TO SIDE WITH INDIA, AND SIGN THE DECLARATION OF ACCESSION^.

INDIA IMMEDIATELY GAVE ORDERS TO WARD OFF THE RAIDERS. 4 KUMAON BATTALION WAS AMONG THE UNITS THAT WERE TO MOVE TO SRINAGAR.

4 KUMAON BATTALION HAS BEEN CALLED IN TO PROTECT THE SRINAGAR AIRSTRIP. DISPATCH ORDERS TO MAJOR SOMNATH SHARMA.

YES, SIR.

I AM SORRY, SOMNATH, BUT YOU CANNOT GO WITH AN INJURY LIKE YOURS. I WILL GET THE ORDER REVERSED.

SIR, MY MEN KNOW THE WAY I FUNCTION AND I KNOW THEM. I MUST GO.

THE BATTALION HAD BEEN LOOKING AFTER INTERNAL SECURITY AT THE TIME. THE OTHER COMPANIES WERE DEPLOYED AT HISSAR, GURGAON AND ROHTAK AREAS.

*SUB-UNIT OF A REGIMENT, CONSISTING OF 140-150 SOLDIERS

^A LEGAL DOCUMENT CREATED IN 1947 TO ENABLE EACH OF THE RULERS OF THE PRINCELY STATES TO JOIN ONE OF THE NEW NATIONS OF INDIA OR PAKISTAN

ON 31 OCTOBER, MAJOR SOMNATH SHARMA, ALONG WITH 70 MEN OF THE DELTA COMPANY, ARRIVED IN SRINAGAR.

THE AIRSTRIP CONNECTS SRINAGAR TO THE REST OF INDIA. IT IS THE FASTEST WAY TO GET SUPPLIES AND TROOPS INTO THE STATE. WE CANNOT LOSE CONTROL OF IT.

YES, SIR!

ON 2 NOVEMBER, MAJOR SOMNATH'S COMPANY WAS JOINED BY COMPANY A (ALPHA), HEADED BY CAPTAIN H.S. BOLINA.

WE HAVE INFORMATION THAT THERE IS A LARGE GROUP OF RAIDERS MOVING IN OVER THESE HILLS.

THE NEXT DAY, TWO COMPANIES HEADED BY MAJOR SOMNATH, ALONG WITH A COMPANY UNDER CAPTAIN RONNIE WOOD FROM 1 KUMAON, WERE SENT TO SURVEY BADGAM.

THAT'S BADGAM VILLAGE. IT IS NEXT TO THE AIRBASE. AN ENEMY THERE WOULD BE A SERIOUS THREAT!

SEARCH THOROUGHLY, WE CAN'T LEAVE ANYTHING TO CHANCE.

AFTER A WHILE –

NOTHING SUSPICIOUS, SIR. ONLY SOME KASHMIRI REFUGEES HIDING IN THE NALA* OVER THERE.

1 KUMAON BATTALION WAS ORDERED TO RETURN TO THE BASE CAMP.

AT AROUND 1430 HRS, THE KASHMIRI REFUGEES STARTED LEAVING –

HEY! STOP! WHERE ARE YOU GOING?

WE'RE JUST GOING HOME.

SUBEDAR, SEARCH THESE MEN.

*A STREAM OR A NARROW RIVER

SUDDENLY –

WHOOM!

AMBUSH! TAKE COVER!

WE ARE ONLY A FEW, BUT WE HAVE TO STOP THEM FROM INFILTRATING!

THE 70 INDIAN SOLDIERS WERE FACING CLOSE TO A 1,000 RAIDERS!

WE ARE UNDER ATTACK AND HAVE BEEN SURROUNDED FROM THREE SIDES. WE NEED REINFORCEMENTS.

DISPATCHING AIR SUPPORT. YOU ARE ADVISED TO STAND DOWN AND NOT TRY ANYTHING RASH.

WE ARE NOT LETTING GO OF OUR POSITION, SIR!

WITH FIGHTER PLANES ON THEIR WAY –

THESE CHALK MARKINGS WILL HELP THE AIR FORCE SPOT OUR POSITION.

SOON –

LOOK! SPITFIRES!

AIR SUPPORT HAD ARRIVED, GIVING THE MEN ON THE GROUND A FEW MINUTES OF RELIEF.

IN SPITE OF THE HELP FROM THE INDIAN AIR FORCE, THE SITUATION ON THE GROUND WAS WORSENING.

KEEP FIGHTING!

THE ENEMY IS FIFTY METRES AWAY. WE ARE OUTNUMBERED. WE'LL FIGHT TO THE LAST MAN AND LAST ROUND.

THE MEN WERE FALLING AND THERE WERE NOT ENOUGH SOLDIERS TO MAN ALL THE MACHINE GUNS.

MAJOR SOMNATH PICKED UP A MACHINE GUN FROM THE GROUND AND LOADED IT WITH A MAGAZINE*.

IGNORING THE PAIN IN HIS ALREADY INJURED ARM, HE CONTINUED TO DESTROY THE ENEMY.

*A CHAMBER THAT CONTAINS BULLETS AND CAN BE LOADED INTO A GUN

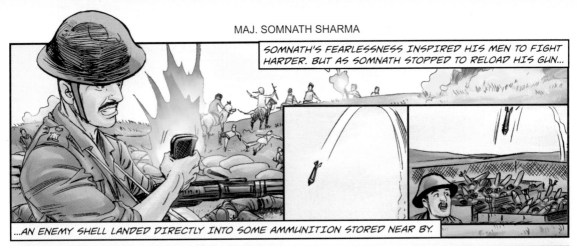

SOMNATH'S FEARLESSNESS INSPIRED HIS MEN TO FIGHT HARDER. BUT AS SOMNATH STOPPED TO RELOAD HIS GUN...

...AN ENEMY SHELL LANDED DIRECTLY INTO SOME AMMUNITION STORED NEAR BY.

WHEN THE SMOKE CLEARED, MAJOR SOMNATH SHARMA LAY AMONG THE DEAD.

SOMNATH WAS JUST 24 YEARS OF AGE WHEN HE DIED.

SPURRED BY HIS LEADER'S DEATH, SEPOY DEWAN SINGH RUSHED HEAD ON...

FOR SOMI SA'AB!

...SHOOTING DOWN THE ENEMY.

MAJOR SOMNATH HAD INSPIRED HIS MEN EVEN WITH HIS LAST BREATH.

I WILL NOT GIVE UP!

NEITHER WILL I!

DEWAN SINGH* ATTACKED THE ENEMY FURIOUSLY...

...TILL HE WAS BROUGHT DOWN BY A BARRAGE OF MACHINE GUN FIRE.

THE INDIANS FOUGHT GALLANTLY.

THE INTRUDERS WERE FORCED TO RETREAT.

THEY ARE FALLING BACK.

WE HAVE WON ENOUGH TIME FOR THE REINFORCEMENTS TO ARRIVE.

BESIDES MAJOR SOMNATH AND SEPOY DEWAN SINGH, THE COMPANY LOST 20 SOLDIERS, WHILE 26 OTHERS WERE WOUNDED.

LET US PULL BACK TO A SECURE LOCATION.

*SEPOY DEWAN SINGH WAS AWARDED THE MAHAVIR CHAKRA FOR HIS ROLE IN THE BATTLE OF BADGAM.

THE BADLY WOUNDED ENEMY RETREATED INTO THE NEARBY HILLS WITHOUT MAKING ANY FURTHER ATTEMPTS AT CAPTURING THE AIRFIELD.

THE BATTLE AT BADGAM STRENGTHENED INDIA'S POSITION IN KASHMIR.

THE ENEMY HAS BEEN DEFEATED AND THE AIRFIELD IS NOW SECURE.

BY HOLDING THEIR GROUND, MAJOR SOMNATH SHARMA AND HIS BAND OF BRAVE MEN SECURED SRINAGAR AND PREVENTED PAKISTAN FROM TAKING OVER KASHMIR.

MAJOR SOMNATH WAS THE FIRST PERSON TO BE AWARDED THE PARAM VIR CHAKRA, INDIA'S HIGHEST GALLANTRY AWARD.

LANCE NAIK KARAM SINGH

YAAA!

DON'T DO THAT, KARAM!

YES! YOU SCARED US!

HA HA! I AM A SOLDIER IN THE ARMY, AND YOU ARE THE ENEMY, YOU HAD BETTER WATCH OUT!

KARAM LOVED PLAYING 'SOLDIER'. HE WOULD OFTEN POUNCE ON HIS FRIENDS, PRETENDING THEY WERE THE ENEMY.

KARAM SINGH WAS THE SON OF A WEALTHY FARMER, SARDAR UTTAM SINGH. HE GREW UP IN THE VILLAGE OF SENHA NEAR SANGRUR IN PUNJAB, LEARNING HOW TO PLOUGH AND SOW SEEDS.

BABUJI, I WANT TO JOIN THE ARMY SOME DAY.

I LIKE THAT! I AM SURE YOU WILL MAKE A BRAVE SOLDIER.

KARAM WORKED TOWARDS HIS GOAL. ON 15 SEPTEMBER, 1941, HE WAS INDUCTED INTO THE SIKH REGIMENT AT MEERUT CANTONMENT AS A SEPOY...

IN 1944, WHEN WORLD WAR II WAS AT ITS PEAK –

OUR UNIT HAS BEEN ORDERED TO THE WAR ZONE. WE LEAVE TOMORROW MORNING.

...AND THEN POSTED TO 1 SIKH REGIMENT IN THE NORTH-EASTERN FRONTIER PROVINCE*.

THE UNIT WAS HEADED TO THE INDO-BURMA BORDER.

I HAVE NEVER SEEN SUCH GREENERY IN MY LIFE. IT'S SO BEAUTIFUL.

WE HAVE TO MOVE ON FOOT FROM THIS POINT. MOVE AHEAD CAREFULLY, THE GROUND IS UNFAMILIAR AND DANGEROUS. THESE JUNGLES ARE VERY THICK AND TREACHEROUS.

*NOW ARUNACHAL PRADESH

THE IMPERIAL JAPANESE ARMY, ALONG WITH THAI FORCES AND BURMESE INSURGENTS, HAD DRIVEN THE BRITISH FORCES OUT OF BURMA.

THE INDIAN SOLDIERS FOUGHT BRAVELY DESPITE MANY OF THEM BEING AFFECTED BY TROPICAL AILMENTS LIKE MALARIA, DYSENTERY AND FEVER.

KARAM SINGH PROVED HIS WORTH IN THE WAR...

...AND WAS AWARDED THE MILITARY MEDAL* FOR HIS CONTRIBUTION.

IN JANUARY, 1948, FOUR MONTHS AFTER INDIA HAD WON HER FREEDOM, PAKISTAN LAUNCHED AN ATTACK ON KASHMIR^.

HARI SINGH, THE MAHARAJA OF KASHMIR, JOINED THE INDIAN UNION. INDIA IMMEDIATELY DEPLOYED ITS ARMED FORCES TO PROTECT THE STATE.

THE SIKH REGIMENT WAS MOVED TO SRINAGAR. THEY WERE TASKED WITH CAPTURING AND THEN DEFENDING THE TOWN OF TITHWAL, WHICH WAS A FEW KILOMETRES FROM SRINAGAR.

KARAM SINGH, WHO HAD BEEN PROMOTED TO LANCE NAIK, AND HIS MEN SET UP A POST ON THE OUTSKIRTS OF TITHWAL.

*A MILITARY DECORATION AWARDED TO PERSONNEL OF THE BRITISH ARMY FOR BRAVERY

^BEFORE THE DECLARATION OF ACCESSION WITH INDIA, KASHMIR WAS AN INDEPENDENT STATE.

KARAM SINGH WAS UNSTOPPABLE. DESPITE THE HEAVY FIRING, HE SHOT DOWN ANY ADVANCING RAIDER AND CONTINUED EVACUATING THE INJURED.

BY 1300 HRS, THE RAIDERS HAD PUT IN A FIFTH ATTACK!

THE ENEMY IS GAINING GROUND.

THEY ARE MOVING IN VERY QUICKLY.

THE ENEMY HAD COME SO CLOSE THAT TWO OF THE RAIDERS HAD MANAGED TO SNEAK UP TO KARAM'S POSITION!

LANCE NAIK KARAM SINGH WAS AWARDED THE PARAM VIR CHAKRA BY INDIA'S FIRST PRESIDENT, DR RAJENDRA PRASAD.

HE WAS THE FIRST NON-POSTHUMOUS PERSON TO WIN THE AWARD.

KARAM SINGH RETIRED FROM THE INDIAN ARMY AS SUBEDAR AND HONORARY CAPTAIN IN 1967.

2/LT RAMA RAGHOBA RANE

THE YEAR WAS 1940, AND WORLD WAR II WAS AT ITS PEAK. RAMA RAGHOBA RANE HAD JUST MADE UP HIS MIND ABOUT WHAT HE WAS GOING TO DO WITH THE REST OF HIS LIFE.

LOOK AT WHAT IT SAYS! FOUR MULE COMPANIES OF THE INDIAN ARMY SERVICE CORPS HAVE JOINED THE BRITISH EXPEDITIONARY FORCES IN FRANCE. CAN YOU BELIEVE IT? THEY'RE GOING TO BE FIGHTING IN EUROPE!

TRUST YOU TO GET EXCITED ABOUT SOMETHING LIKE THAT, RAMA. THOSE MEN ARE RISKING THEIR LIVES – NOT GOING ON VACATION!

BUT WHAT COULD BE MORE FULFILLING? TRAVELLING ACROSS THE WORLD, FIGHTING THE ENEMY SHOULDER TO SHOULDER WITH BRAVE MEN – CAN YOU THINK OF A BETTER ADVENTURE?

I'VE MADE MY DECISION! I'M JOINING THE ARMY!

OH! HERE HE IS NOW!

HAVE YOU SPOKEN TO YOUR FATHER ABOUT THIS?

HOPE HE AGREES.

I WILL. TONIGHT.

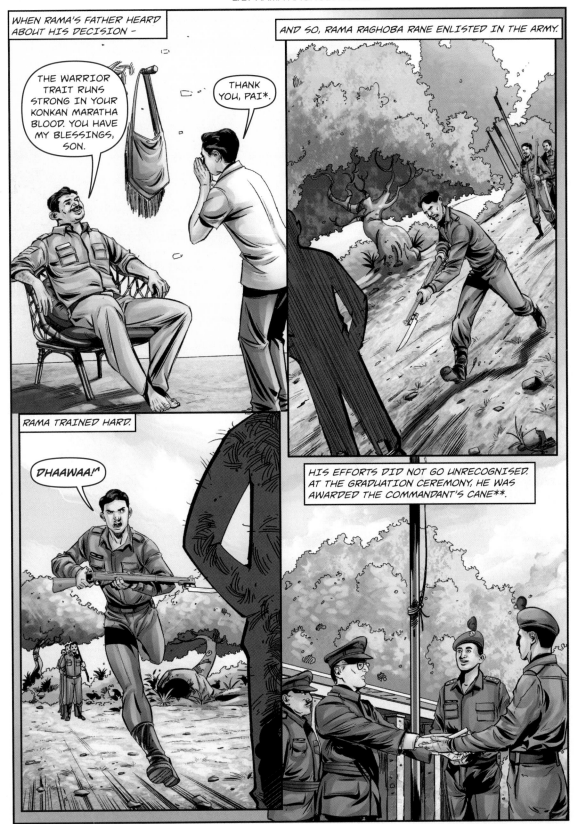

*'FATHER', IN KONKANI
^"ATTACK!"

**AWARD GIVEN TO BEST CADET
DURING TRAINING PERIOD

BEFORE LONG, HE WAS IN ACTIVE SERVICE, FIGHTING THE JAPANESE IN BURMA.

AERIAL ATTACK! TAKE COVER.

BACK IN THE BUNKERS –

PACK YOUR BAGS, RANE. YOU HAVE BEEN RECOMMENDED FOR J.C.O.* TRAINING IN POONA^. YOU'VE BEEN ASSIGNED TO THE BOMBAY ENGINEERS.

THANK YOU, SIR!

CONGRATULATIONS.

RANE'S PROWESS IN BATTLE DID NOT GO UNNOTICED. HE WAS PROMOTED TO THE RANK OF NAIK.

RISING TO THE RANK OF J.C.O. IN THE PRE-INDEPENDENCE ARMY WAS NO MEAN FEAT FOR A SOLDIER.

TRAINING WITH THE BOMBAY ENGINEERS WAS RIGOROUS. IN WARTIME, THE ENGINEERING CORPS PROVIDES SUPPORT TO TROOPS BY BUILDING ROADS, HELIPADS, BRIDGES, ETC. THEY ALSO CLEAR MINES.

GENTLEMEN, TODAY WE STUDY THE DIFFERENT METHODS OF PLANTING EXPLOSIVE CHARGES TO EFFECTIVELY DESTROY CONCRETE STRUCTURES.

*JUNIOR COMMISSIONED OFFICER

^NOW PUNE

UNFORTUNATELY, THE ARMED FORCES OF INDIA DID NOT HAVE MUCH TIME TO SAVOUR THEIR FREEDOM.

IN OCTOBER, 1947, TRIBAL MILITIA AND IRREGULAR PAKISTANI FORCES SWEPT INTO KASHMIR, INTENDING TO TAKE SRINAGAR.

Muzaffarabad ☐
Islamabad ☐
☐ Srinagar

DURING THE TURBULENT PARTITION OF BRITISH INDIA INTO INDIA AND PAKISTAN, THERE WERE A LOT OF POLITICAL DISAGREEMENTS. CHIEF AMONG THEM WAS THE CONFLICT OVER THE STATUS OF THE PRINCELY STATE OF JAMMU & KASHMIR.

THE STATE FORCES AT THE BORDERS WERE QUICKLY DEFEATED BY THE TRIBALS. MAHARAJA HARI SINGH SOUGHT HELP FROM INDIA AND SIGNED THE INSTRUMENT OF ACCESSION.

INDIAN TROOPS REINFORCED THE STATE FORCES, AND THE SKIRMISHES QUICKLY ESCALATED INTO THE 1947 INDO-PAK WAR.

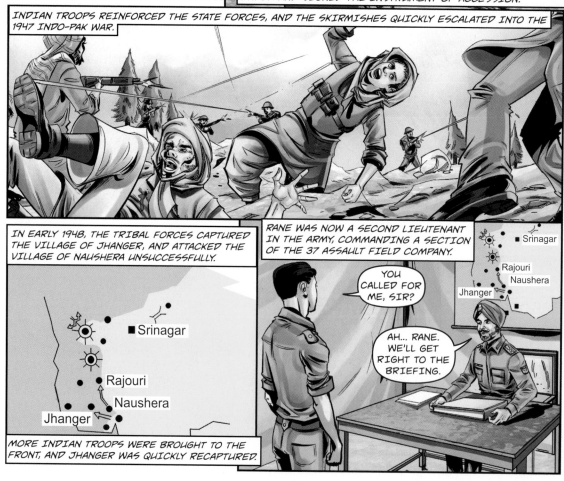

IN EARLY 1948, THE TRIBAL FORCES CAPTURED THE VILLAGE OF JHANGER, AND ATTACKED THE VILLAGE OF NAUSHERA UNSUCCESSFULLY.

■ Srinagar
● Rajouri
Naushera
Jhanger

MORE INDIAN TROOPS WERE BROUGHT TO THE FRONT, AND JHANGER WAS QUICKLY RECAPTURED.

RANE WAS NOW A SECOND LIEUTENANT IN THE ARMY, COMMANDING A SECTION OF THE 37 ASSAULT FIELD COMPANY.

■ Srinagar
Rajouri
Naushera
Jhanger ●

YOU CALLED FOR ME, SIR?

AH... RANE. WE'LL GET RIGHT TO THE BRIEFING.

THE RAIDERS ARE TERRORISING INDIAN CITIZENS IN RAJOURI. THE PAKISTANI ARMY HAS DESTROYED THE RAJOURI-PUNJ HIGHWAY. OUR TANK COLUMN WILL BE TAKING THE OLD MUGHAL ROUTE FROM NAUSHERA TO GET THERE.

UNDERSTOOD, SIR.

IT'S HILLY TERRAIN. THE ENEMY HAS BEEN ESTABLISHING ROADBLOCKS...

...YOU AND YOUR MEN HAVE BEEN ASSIGNED AS THE CLEARING PARTY.

WE'RE READY TO GO, SIR!

8 APRIL, 1948, AT 1100 HRS: 2/LT RANE AND HIS MEN WERE LEADING THE WAY FOR THE TANK COLUMN AS THEY ADVANCED TOWARDS THEIR FIRST STRATEGICALLY IMPORTANT DESTINATION, NADPUR.

ANTI-TANK MINES SUNK IN THE GROUND HAD TO BE LOCATED WITH MINE DETECTORS. THE TASK NEEDED INTENSE CONCENTRATION.

WE'RE ALMOST AT NADPUR, AND IT HAS BEEN REASONABLY QUIET SO FAR.

KEEP YOUR GUARD UP, SOLDIER! REPORTS SAY THAT THE ENEMY HAS A PICKET IN THE BARWALI RIDGE. WE'LL HAVE TO CAPTURE THE RIDGE IF WE ARE TO ADVANCE FURTHER!

SOON –

INCOMING!

GET DOWN, MEN! ENEMY FIRE!

BOOM!

AAAARGH!

THE ENEMY WAS RAINING 3-INCH MORTARS. THE MINE-CLEARING MEN WERE SITTING DUCKS!

29

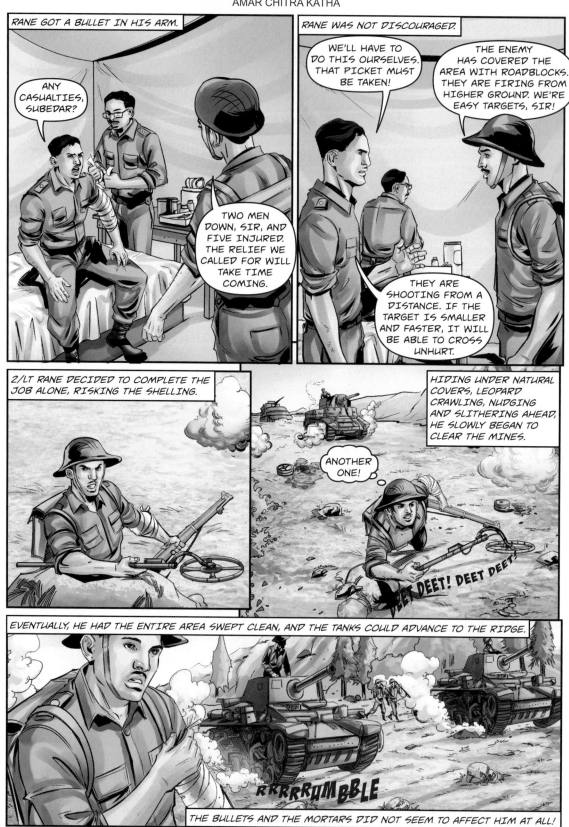

RANE GOT A BULLET IN HIS ARM.

ANY CASUALTIES, SUBEDAR?

TWO MEN DOWN, SIR, AND FIVE INJURED. THE RELIEF WE CALLED FOR WILL TAKE TIME COMING.

RANE WAS NOT DISCOURAGED.

WE'LL HAVE TO DO THIS OURSELVES. THAT PICKET MUST BE TAKEN!

THE ENEMY HAS COVERED THE AREA WITH ROADBLOCKS. THEY ARE FIRING FROM HIGHER GROUND. WE'RE EASY TARGETS, SIR!

THEY ARE SHOOTING FROM A DISTANCE. IF THE TARGET IS SMALLER AND FASTER, IT WILL BE ABLE TO CROSS UNHURT.

2/LT RANE DECIDED TO COMPLETE THE JOB ALONE, RISKING THE SHELLING.

HIDING UNDER NATURAL COVERS, LEOPARD CRAWLING, NUDGING AND SLITHERING AHEAD, HE SLOWLY BEGAN TO CLEAR THE MINES.

ANOTHER ONE!

DEET DEET! DEET DEET!

EVENTUALLY, HE HAD THE ENTIRE AREA SWEPT CLEAN, AND THE TANKS COULD ADVANCE TO THE RIDGE.

RRRRRUMBBLE

THE BULLETS AND THE MORTARS DID NOT SEEM TO AFFECT HIM AT ALL!

BY 1600 HRS, INDIANS HAD CAPTURED THE BARWALI RIDGE AND OVERPOWERED THE RAIDERS.

THIS IS JUST THE BEGINNING, RANE.

WE ARE READY TO START WORK AGAIN, SIR.

THE ENEMY WAS STILL PRESENT. THE ROAD AHEAD HAD BEEN DESTROYED. A DIVERSION HAD TO BE MADE FOR THE TANKS TO PROCEED.

RANE AND HIS PARTY WORKED TILL 2200 HRS THAT NIGHT IN FULL VIEW OF THE ENEMY AND UNDER MACHINE GUN FIRE.

9 APRIL: RANE AND HIS MEN WORKED FROM 0600 HRS TO 1500 HRS TO MAKE THE DIVERSION. THEN –

READY TO PROCEED, SIR.

VERY GOOD. GET IN, WE'RE READY TO GO.

BUT ABOUT HALF A KILOMETRE AHEAD –

PINE TREES ARE BLOCKING THE ROAD UP AHEAD, SIR!

STOP THE VEHICLE! THIS WON'T TAKE LONG.

RANE SET A CHARGE UNDER THE TREES TO BLAST THEM OUT OF THE WAY.

DONE! GET BACK NOW – TELL THE COMMANDER WE'LL BE READY TO MOVE IN A FEW MINUTES!

BOOM!

THE SAME STORY WAS REPEATED ABOUT 300M AWAY.

AT 1700 HRS –

IT'S A DEMOLISHED CULVERT THIS TIME, SIR.

SHOULDN'T BE A PROBLEM, SUBEDAR. LET'S GET ON WITH IT.

BUT BEFORE HE COULD START WORK, THE ENEMY OPENED UP WITH THEIR MACHINE GUNS.

COME ON, MEN! WE HAVE TO MOVE ON! WE HAVE A JOB TO DO!

YES, SIR!

UNDER RANE'S LEADERSHIP, THE MEN CREATED A DIVERSION FOR THE TANKS TO PASS THROUGH.

BY 1815 HRS, THEY HAD CLEARED NUMEROUS ROADBLOCKS AND LIGHT WAS FADING FAST, BUT THEIR BIGGEST CHALLENGE STILL LAY IN FRONT OF THEM.

LOOK AT THE SIZE OF THOSE PINE TREES! AND THEY'RE SURELY SURROUNDED BY MINES!

FIVE TREES – BUT THAT'S NOT ALL. THEY'LL BE COVERING THE ROADBLOCK WITH MACHINE GUNS.

RANE BEGAN CLEARING THE MINES, UNFAZED BY ENEMY FIRE.

SIR! THE COLUMN COMMANDER SAYS WE'RE DONE FOR THE DAY. HE'S TAKING THE TANKS TO A HARBOUR AREA.

DID YOU TELL HIM THAT WE CAN GO ON WORKING THROUGH THE NIGHT?

YES, SIR. HE DOESN'T WANT TO TAKE THE RISK.

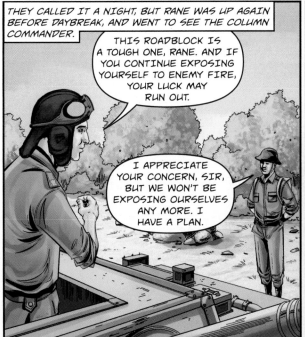

THEY CALLED IT A NIGHT, BUT RANE WAS UP AGAIN BEFORE DAYBREAK, AND WENT TO SEE THE COLUMN COMMANDER.

THIS ROADBLOCK IS A TOUGH ONE, RANE. AND IF YOU CONTINUE EXPOSING YOURSELF TO ENEMY FIRE, YOUR LUCK MAY RUN OUT.

I APPRECIATE YOUR CONCERN, SIR, BUT WE WON'T BE EXPOSING OURSELVES ANY MORE. I HAVE A PLAN.

A PLAN?

I THINK THERE'S A WAY FOR MY MEN TO WORK UP TO THE ROAD BLOCK WHILE BEING SUPPORTED BY OUR TANKS.

GO ON.

OUR TANKS ARE LINED UP IN A COLUMN AND THEY NEED TO MOVE AHEAD. I WANT PERMISSION TO HIDE UNDER THE LEAD TANK AND USE IT AS A COVER.

AS THE TANKS MOVE FORWARD, I WILL SWEEP THE GROUND FOR MINES AND NEUTRALISE THEM BEFORE MOVING ON. WHEN WE REACH THE ROADBLOCK, I WILL LAY EXPLOSIVES TO BLAST IT AND CLEAR THE WAY.

HMM... THAT'S A DARING PLAN! HOW WILL YOU LET MY DRIVER KNOW THAT IT'S SAFE TO CROSS AFTER YOU HAVE EXTRACTED THE MINE?

SIR, WE WILL MAKE A ROPE SIGNAL. AS SOON AS I CLEAR A MINE I WILL PULL THE LEFT ROPE AND HE CAN MOVE AHEAD. WHEN I PULL THE RIGHT ROPE HE NEEDS TO STOP.

THE COMMANDER GAVE RANE PERMISSION TO TRY HIS UNUSUAL IDEA. BY 0445 HRS, THEY WERE RARING TO GO.

IS IT WORKING?

YES, IT IS. GET INTO POSITION.

THEY SET OFF.

RRRRRUMBLE

GOT ONE!

TUG

DEET DEET!

STOP! STOP! HE'S PULLING THE ROPE ON THE RIGHT.

YES, SIR!

RANE PATIENTLY AND PAINSTAKINGLY WENT ABOUT HIS WORK.

THE ROPE SIGNALS WORKED VERY WELL, AND HE COULD EASILY COMMUNICATE WITH THE OCCUPANTS OF THE TANK.

DONE!

RANE STEADILY CLEARED THE WAY FOR A SINGLE TANK COLUMN TO PASS THROUGH.

THUNK

I THOUGHT THAT BUSH LOOKED SUSPICIOUS!

DEET DEET!

ANOTHER ONE OUT OF THE WAY.

GO! GO!

IT WAS NOT LONG BEFORE THEY REACHED A ROADBLOCK.

IT'S ALL UP TO ME NOW. I CAN'T LET MY BROTHERS DOWN!

WHOOM!

35

AT 1400 HRS, AS RANE WAS BUSY CLEARING THE ROAD TO CHINGAS, A VILLAGE 22.5KM FROM RAJOURI –

-KZZT-TANKS ARE REACHING -KZZT- CHINGAS. OVER.

THEY ARE ALMOST HERE. WE HAVE TO OPEN THE ROAD AS SOON AS POSSIBLE, MEN!

RANE AND HIS MEN WORKED TIRELESSLY, WITHOUT FOOD OR REST, TILL 2100 HRS THAT NIGHT.

ON 11 APRIL, 1948, BY 1100 HRS, THE ROAD TO CHINGAS WAS OPENED.

THEY'RE HERE! THEY'RE HERE!

AMAZING! RANE'S DONE IT AGAIN, FASTER THAN ANYONE EXPECTED!

WELCOME TO CHINGAS, RANE. WOULD YOU LIKE TO REST FOR A WHILE?

WE'LL REST AFTER WE REACH RAJOURI AND RELIEVE THE CITIZENS THERE, SIR!

RANE CONTINUED CLEARING THE ROADS FROM CHINGAS TO RAJOURI TILL 2200 HRS.

THE INDIAN ARMY SOON LIBERATED RAJOURI, WITH 2/LT RAGHOBA RANE PLAYING A VITAL PART IN THE EFFORT.

FOR HIS VALOUR AND SERVICE WITH COMPLETE DISREGARD FOR PERSONAL SAFETY, HE WAS AWARDED THE PARAM VIR CHAKRA.

NAIK YADUNATH SINGH

SHAHJAHANPUR, UTTAR PRADESH, PRE-INDEPENDENT INDIA

YADU! YADU! YOU CAN BEAT HIM!

URGH!

GO, YADU!

AAH!

DONE IT!

BHAIYYA, I WANT TO BE A WRESTLER WHEN I GROW UP!

YADUNATH SINGH WAS THE YOUNGEST OF SEVEN BROTHERS.

SEVERAL YEARS LATER, YADUNATH SINGH HAD NOT GIVEN UP ON HIS AMBITION.

BUT I WANT TO BE A WRESTLER!

AND HOW DO YOU PLAN TO SUPPORT A FAMILY, YADU?

I'VE DECIDED NOT TO MARRY.

YOU MUST GET MARRIED!

WHEN HIS PROTESTS SEEMED COMPLETELY FUTILE...

...YADUNATH DECIDED TO LEAVE HIS VILLAGE.

39

SOON, THE PLUCKY YOUNG MAN DECIDED TO JOIN THE ARMY. IT WOULD GIVE HIM THE PHYSICALLY ACTIVE LIFE HE WANTED.

ON 21 NOVEMBER, 1941, YADUNATH SINGH ENROLLED IN 1 RAJPUT REGIMENT AS A SEPOY.

AN ACTIVE AND FIT PERSON, HE PLAYED HARD AND TRAINED HARDER.

YADUNATH LOVED BEING IN THE ARMY.

ONE DAY, WHEN ALL THE SOLDIERS WERE HAVING LUNCH –

YOU! COME AND SEE ME IN MY OFFICE TOMORROW MORNING.

YES, SIR!

THE NEXT DAY –

ALL THE SOLDIERS WERE SITTING TOGETHER AND HAVING THEIR MEAL. WHY WERE YOU EATING SEPARATELY?

I DON'T EAT MEAT, SIR.

I EAT ONLY VEGETABLES.

WHAT?! A VEGETARIAN! EATING ONLY VEGETABLES WILL MAKE YOU WEAK. THERE'S NO PLACE FOR WEAK SOLDIERS IN MY REGIMENT!

I AM NOT WEAK, SIR. I CAN WRESTLE TWO SOLDIERS SIMULTANEOUSLY, AND WIN.

IS THAT SO? LET'S CHECK THAT OUT. THE MATCH WILL BE TOMORROW.

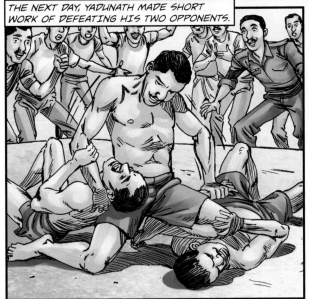

THE NEXT DAY, YADUNATH MADE SHORT WORK OF DEFEATING HIS TWO OPPONENTS.

THE BRITISH OFFICER HAD TO EAT HIS WORDS, AND YADUNATH CONTINUED TO EAT HIS VEGETABLES!

SEVERAL YEARS LATER, AN INDEPENDENT INDIA WAS ENGAGED WITH HER NEIGHBOUR, PAKISTAN, IN A BATTLE OVER TERRITORY IN KASHMIR.

ON 24 DECEMBER, 1947, PAKISTAN HAD CAPTURED JHANGAR. THIS HAD MADE THE POSITION OF THE PAKISTANI ARMY MORE ADVANTAGEOUS.

IN JANUARY, 1948, THE INDIAN ARMY CONDUCTED SEVERAL OPERATIONS TO ENSURE THAT THERE WOULD BE NO ENEMY BUILDUP ALONG THE BORDER.

IN THE MEANTIME, PAKISTAN'S ARMY HAD ALREADY MADE FOUR FRONTAL ATTACKS ON TAINDHAR IN KASHMIR, BUT THEY HAD BEEN UNSUCCESSFUL. THE INDIAN ARMY REALISED THAT AN ATTACK ON THE NEARBY NAUSHERA POST WAS IMMINENT AND ESTABLISHED STRONG PICKETS IN DEFENCE.

SURE ENOUGH, THE PAKISTAN ARMY SWITCHED ITS EFFORTS TO NAUSHERA. THE LEFT FLANK OF THE NAUSHERA DEFENCES, NO. 2 PICKET, WAS A VITAL POST. A GROUP OF NINE MEN OF 1 RAJPUT HELD THIS SPOT. THEY WERE LED BY YADUNATH SINGH, NOW NAIK YADUNATH SINGH.

6 FEBRUARY, 1948, WAS PROBABLY THE LONGEST DAY IN THE LIVES OF NAIK YADUNATH SINGH AND HIS EIGHT SOLDIERS. THE ENEMY HAD CREPT UP CLOSE TO THEIR PICKET BEFORE DAYBREAK.

AS THE FIRST RAYS OF SUNLIGHT HIT THE GROUND, THE SOLDIERS OF 1 RAJPUT SPOTTED SOME MOVEMENT.

ENEMY AHEAD!

YADUNATH SINGH RADIOED HIS BASE CAMP IMMEDIATELY.

....WE ARE GREATLY OUTNUMBERED, SIR. WE WILL REQUIRE ADDITIONAL AMMUNITION.

I'M SORRY, NAIK YADU. IT WILL BE A WHILE BEFORE MORE AMMO REACHES YOU.

A STRAIGHT-TALKER, YADUNATH TOLD HIS MEN EXACTLY WHAT TO EXPECT.

THE ENEMY CAN ATTACK AT ANY TIME. AND WE HAVE TO MAKE DO WITH THE AMMO WE HAVE HERE. MAKE EVERY BULLET COUNT. WE CANNOT GIVE UP OUR POST.

THEY ARE TOO MANY!

SO WE'LL HAVE TO RELY ON OUR WITS.

THERE ARE ONLY NINE OF US, NAIK YADU.

YES. AND WE KNOW THAT. BUT THEY DON'T. NOW, HERE'S WHAT WE'LL DO....

NAIK YADUNATH HAD A PLAN.

THE ENEMY SOLDIERS STARTED FIRING AT 0640 HRS. BEFORE LONG, THE TWO GROUPS WERE IN THE THICK OF A BATTLE.

YOU SAID THERE WERE JUST A HANDFUL OF THEM!

MAYBE THEY GOT REINFORCEMENTS?

THE ENEMY WAS CONFUSED...

...AND THAT WAS EXACTLY WHAT YADUNATH SINGH HAD HOPED AND EXPECTED.

YADUNATH'S PLAN HAD BEEN DARING.

....HERE'S WHAT WE'LL DO. POSITION YOURSELVES AS FAR APART FROM EACH OTHER AS POSSIBLE. KEEP MOVING TO DIFFERENT POSITIONS. IT'LL MAKE US LOOK LIKE WE'RE A LARGER GROUP....

THE TRICK WORKED.

THEY'RE RETREATING!

THEY'LL BE BACK. WE WILL HAVE TO STOP THEM AGAIN.

SURE ENOUGH, THE ENEMY SOON LAUNCHED ANOTHER ATTACK.

WE HAVE TO USE THE GRENADES ACCURATELY. WE CANNOT WASTE EVEN A SINGLE ONE.

YADUNATH AND HIS TEAM MAINTAINED THEIR STRATEGY, BUT THE SECOND ENCOUNTER WAS A LOT MORE INTENSE THAN THE FIRST.

UNGH!

GUNNER, YOU HAVE A CLEAR....

YADUNATH NOTICED THAT HIS BREN-GUNNER HAD FALLEN AND WAS GRIEVOUSLY INJURED.

HE LOOKED AROUND AND SAW THAT MOST OF HIS SOLDIERS HAD FALLEN.

GET UP! DON'T GIVE UP! FIGHT!

HE TOOK THE BREN GUN AND STARTED FIRING. INSPIRED BY YADUNATH'S WORDS, THE SOLDIERS FOUGHT WITH RENEWED VIGOUR.

THE ENEMY WAS FORCED TO RETREAT AGAIN...

...BUT ALL NINE SOLDIERS WERE LEFT WOUNDED.

YADUNATH SINGH HAD INJURED HIS RIGHT ARM.

BEFORE ANY OF THE OTHERS HAD TIME TO RECOVER, THERE WAS A THIRD ATTACK.

YADUNATH SINGH HAD TO FACE THE ENEMY ALONE.

HE CHARGED AT THE ENEMY WITH THE FINAL RESERVES OF HIS STRENGTH.

UH!

I THOUGHT THEY WERE ALL DEAD.

SEEING THE ENEMY TAKEN BY SURPRISE, YADUNATH THREW THE LAST OF THE GRENADES...

...BUT HE COULD NOT STOP THEM ADVANCING TOWARDS NO. 2 PICKET.

46

WHAT FOLLOWED WAS A DISPLAY OF UNRELENTING HAND-TO-HAND COMBAT BOTH FIERCE AND RUTHLESS.

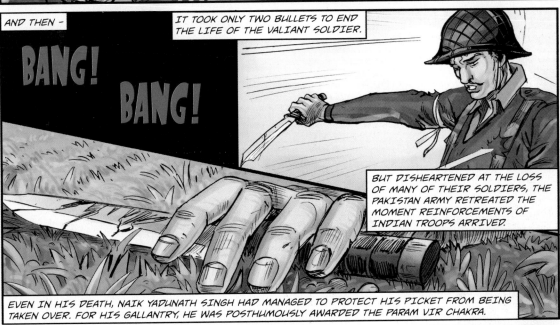

AND THEN –

BANG!

BANG!

IT TOOK ONLY TWO BULLETS TO END THE LIFE OF THE VALIANT SOLDIER.

BUT DISHEARTENED AT THE LOSS OF MANY OF THEIR SOLDIERS, THE PAKISTAN ARMY RETREATED THE MOMENT REINFORCEMENTS OF INDIAN TROOPS ARRIVED.

EVEN IN HIS DEATH, NAIK YADUNATH SINGH HAD MANAGED TO PROTECT HIS PICKET FROM BEING TAKEN OVER. FOR HIS GALLANTRY, HE WAS POSTHUMOUSLY AWARDED THE PARAM VIR CHAKRA.

EVEN TODAY, THE PEOPLE OF SHAHJAHANPUR PROUDLY RETELL THE STORY OF THE VALIANT SOLDIER AND CELEBRATE HIS BIRTH AND DEATH ANNIVERSARIES WITH GREAT HONOUR.

....HE NOTICED THAT THERE WAS SOME MOVEMENT NEAR THE....

CHM PIRU SINGH SHEKHAWAT

A YEAR HAD PASSED SINCE INDIA GAINED INDEPENDENCE FROM BRITISH RULE, BUT TENSIONS WERE HIGH ON THE JAMMU & KASHMIR BORDER.

PAKISTAN CONTINUES TO ATTACK DESPITE OUR BEATING THEM BACK REPEATEDLY.

THE OFFICER COMMANDING OF DELTA COMPANY, 6 RAJPUTANA RIFLES, WAS CONSULTING WITH HIS MEN. ONE OF THEM WAS C.H.M.* PIRU SINGH SHEKHAWAT.

PAKISTANI RANGERS HAD OCCUPIED THE TITHWAL REGION IN A BID TO TAKE OVER KASHMIR. 6 RAJPUTANA RIFLES HAD THE TASK OF DRIVING THEM OUT.

THE ENEMY CONTROLS TWO OF OUR BASES ON DARAPARI HILL. WE CAN'T MAKE PROGRESS UNTIL WE CLEAR THEM.

IT'S 10,000FT TILL FIRST BASE.

THAT'S RIGHT, PIRU.

PIRU HAD ENROLLED IN THE REGIMENT ON HIS 18TH BIRTHDAY IN 1936. NOW, 12 YEARS LATER, HE FACED HIS TOUGHEST CHALLENGE.

OUR RADIO SIGNALS ARE BEING MONITORED. THEY KNOW OUR PLANS, PIRU.

WE HAVE TO DEFEAT THEM. FAR TOO MANY INNOCENT LIVES HAVE BEEN LOST ALREADY.

THOUGH THE ENEMY WAS FAR AWAY, THEIR NIGHT TRAINING COMPELLED THEM TO SPEAK IN HUSHED TONES.

SOLDIERS, WE WILL LAUNCH AN ATTACK ON THE FIRST BASE TONIGHT. THE OTHER TROOPS WILL PROVIDE COVERING FIRE.

*COMPANY HAVILDAR MAJOR

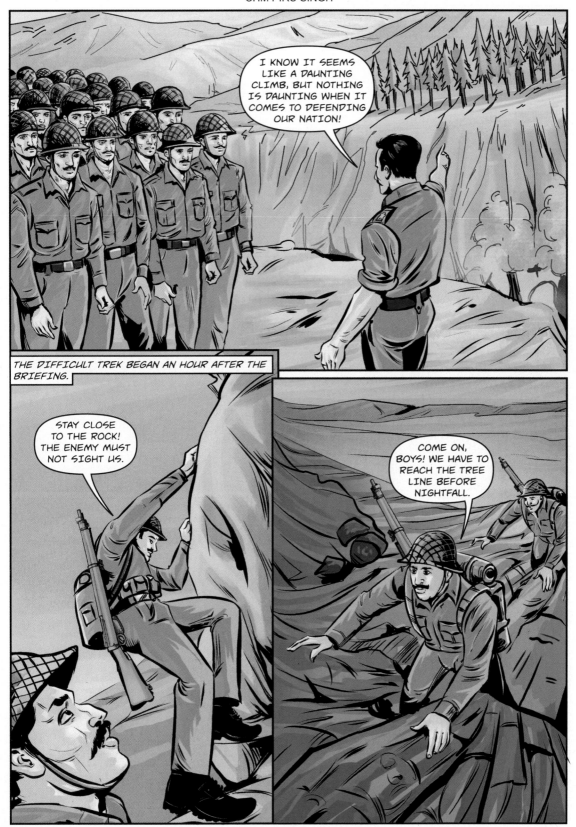

WHEN THEY REACHED THE TREES –

STOP! WE SHALL SPEND THE NIGHT HERE. AT DAWN, WE ATTACK.

THE MEN BEGAN DIGGING TRENCHES WITH EXTREME CAUTION.

BE VERY QUIET!

THE SOLDIERS WERE NOT EVEN ALLOWED TO LIGHT A MATCH FOR FEAR OF BEING SEEN BY THE ENEMY.

NOW WE WAIT TILL WE GET THE SIGNAL TO ATTACK.

AFTER A WHILE, PIRU WAS SUMMONED BY THE OFFICER COMMANDING.

THE SUPPORTING FIRE HAS NOT YET ARRIVED, BUT OUR ORDERS ARE TO GO AHEAD.

SIR.

PIRU ASSESSED THE CLIMB THEY HAD TO MAKE TO GET TO THE ENEMY.

THE PATH IS VERY NARROW AND THE PAKISTANI BUNKERS OVERLOOK THE ENTIRE STRETCH.

WE WILL BE EXPOSED THE WHOLE TIME. WE MUST REMAIN EXTREMELY QUIET IF WE WANT TO TAKE THEM BY SURPRISE!

THE ATTACK WAS LAUNCHED AT 0130 HRS ON 18 JULY, 1948.

TAKE COVER!

TRA-GA-DA-GA

THE PAKISTANI SOLDIERS WERE RELENTLESS. WITHIN 30 MINUTES, THE INDIANS HAD SUFFERED 51 CASUALTIES.

WE'VE ALREADY LOST HALF OUR SOLDIERS.

THAT M.M.G.* BASE IS CAUSING US A LOT OF DAMAGE. I MUST DISABLE IT!

WITHOUT HESITATION, PIRU CHARGED TOWARDS THE BUNKER. BUT BEFORE HE COULD MAKE IT...

BOOM!

...A GRENADE EXPLODED NEAR HIM.

*MEDIUM MACHINE GUN

THE WAR CRY OF THE REGIMENT GAVE HIM STRENGTH.

THE ENEMY SEEMED POWERLESS IN FRONT OF HIS CHARGE.

AAAAH!

BY THE TIME PIRU HAD CLEARED THE FIRST M.M.G. BASE, ALL HIS FELLOW SOLDIERS LAY DEAD OR WOUNDED.

IT IS UP TO ME TO ENSURE THE SUCCESS OF THE MISSION!

BUT JUST THEN –

UGHHH!

BLEEDING FROM HIS INJURIES AND WITH ALL HIS OWN AMMUNITION OVER, PIRU HAD ONLY ONE THOUGHT –

I MUST NOT GIVE UP!

HE FOUND SOME AMMUNITION THAT WAS LEFT BEHIND IN THE BUNKER.

GRENADES! JUST WHAT I NEED.

HE CHARGED TOWARDS THE NEXT BUNKER.

TAKE THIS... AND THIS!

BOOM!

UNGHHH!

PIRU HAD NOW CLEARED TWO M.M.G. BASES BY HIMSELF. BUT AS HE MADE HIS WAY TOWARDS A THIRD BUNKER –

AAH!

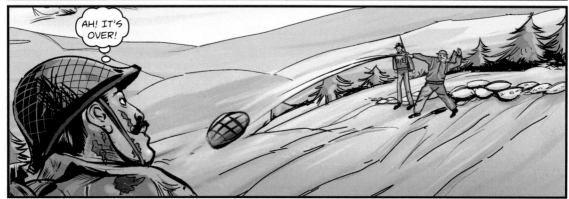

PIRU HAS DONE IT! THE PAKISTANIS ARE ALL DEAD!

BUT PIRU HAD BREATHED HIS LAST TOO.

PIRU'S BRAVE ACT GAVE THE INDIANS A MAJOR ADVANTAGE. AFTER THE WAR, PRIME MINISTER JAWAHARLAL NEHRU WROTE TO PIRU'S MOTHER, SAYING –

'HE PAID WITH HIS LIFE FOR HIS SINGULARLY BRAVE ACT, BUT HE LEFT FOR THE REST OF HIS COMRADES A UNIQUE EXAMPLE OF SINGLE-HANDED BRAVERY AND DETERMINED COLD COURAGE. THE COUNTRY IS GRATEFUL FOR THIS SACRIFICE MADE IN THE SERVICE OF THE MOTHERLAND, AND IT IS OUR PRAYER THAT THIS MAY GIVE YOU SOME PEACE AND SOLACE.'

PIRU SINGH SHEKHAWAT WAS AWARDED THE PARAM VIR CHAKRA POSTHUMOUSLY FOR HIS HEROIC DEEDS.

CAPTAIN G.S. SALARIA

CAPTAIN G.S. SALARIA WAS RIGHT.

WE'RE GOING TO THE CONGO, GENTLEMEN.

AS PART OF THE 99TH INFANTRY BRIGADE, OUR BATTALION IS GOING TO BE PARTICIPATING IN A UNITED NATIONS PEACEKEEPING MISSION*.

DOWN HERE IS KATANGA – RICH IN NATURAL RESOURCES. WEST EUROPEAN NATIONS STILL HAVE BUSINESS INTERESTS IN THIS REGION.

"THE REPUBLIC OF CONGO WON ITS INDEPENDENCE FROM BELGIUM ON 30 JUNE, 1960. THE NEW GOVERNMENT SET UP ITS CAPITAL IN LEOPOLDVILLE^."

Joseph Kasavubu

Patrice Lumumba

ON 10 JULY, 1960, BELGIUM SENT ITS ARMY INTO THE CONGO, CLAIMING THAT THEY WANTED TO PROTECT THE INTERESTS OF BELGIANS STAYING BACK.

"ON 11 JULY, MOISE TSHOMBE, THE PROVINCIAL PRESIDENT OF KATANGA, DECIDED TO SECEDE** FROM THE REPUBLIC OF CONGO. WITH FULL SUPPORT FROM BELGIUM, OF COURSE.

THOUGH THE BELGIANS HAVE WITHDRAWN, THEY ARE MAINTAINING A MILITARY PRESENCE IN KATANGA.

BUT THERE ARE VIOLENT CLASHES BETWEEN THE CONGOLESE FORCES AND THE REBELS. SO, THE U.N. HAS DECIDED TO SEND TROOPS TO MAINTAIN ORDER THERE.

"AT THE REQUEST OF PRESIDENT KASAVUBU AND PRIME MINISTER LUMUMBA, THE UNITED NATIONS DECIDED TO INTERVENE IN THE MATTER. IN AUGUST, THEY ORDERED THE BELGIAN ARMY OUT OF CONGO."

S S MAITRA

*AN INTERNATIONAL MILITARY FORCE SENT BY THE UNITED NATIONS TO MAINTAIN A TRUCE BETWEEN COUNTRIES OR COMMUNITIES

^NOW KNOWN AS KINSHASA
**TO WITHDRAW FORMALLY FROM AN ALLIANCE

AT THE BATTALION OFFICERS' MESS –

CAPTAIN! CAPTAIN SALARIA!

MY GOD! WHAT HAPPENED OUT THERE?

WE WERE SET UPON BY THE LOCALS. MOISE TSHOMBE HAS THEM WORKED UP INTO A FRENZY!

THOSE CIVILIANS NEED TO BE TAUGHT NOT TO MESS WITH THE ARMY!

EASY, LIEUTENANT. WE'RE HERE TO KEEP THE PEACE. LT COL MAITRA WILL KNOW HOW TO HANDLE THE MATTER DIPLOMATICALLY.

ON 29 APRIL, LT COL S.S. MAITRA INVITED GRAND CHIEF KASENGO NYEMBO OF THE NATIVE BALUBA TRIBE TO THE BATTALION OFFICERS' MESS.

WELCOME TO OUR HEADQUARTERS, CHIEF NYEMBO.

THE IDEA WAS TO ENGAGE WITH THE LOCAL PEOPLE DIRECTLY.

WE WOULD BE HONOURED IF YOU ACCEPTED THIS GIFT AS A SYMBOL OF OUR EVERLASTING FRIENDSHIP.

SPLENDID! A SILVER DAGGER!

A KHUKRI, SIR! IT'S THE CLASSIC GURKHA WEAPON. YOU CAN SEE TWO OF THEM CROSSED ON THE INSIGNIA OF OUR REGIMENT.

AH, THANK YOU!

I HAVE A GIFT FOR YOUR BATTALION, COLONEL. A SAMPLE OF THE IVORY WE BALUBA PRIDE OURSELVES ON.

THE VISIT OF THE GRAND CHIEF WAS WELL PUBLICISED, AND WAS VERY EFFECTIVE IN CURBING ANTI-U.N. FEELINGS IN KATANGA.

LOOK! THIS ARTICLE MAKES IT SEEM LIKE THE LOCALS MIGHT EVEN HAVE STARTED TO LIKE US A LITTLE!

GREAT. NOW ALL WE HAVE TO WORRY ABOUT ARE MOISE TSHOMBE'S GENDARMERIES.

THE BELGIAN ARMY HAD WITHDRAWN FROM MOST OF THE COUNTRY, BUT THEY HAD TRAINED SEVERAL KATANGESE REBEL UNITS AND LEFT WESTERN EUROPEAN MERCENARIES IN CHARGE OF THEM. THESE WERE KNOWN AS GENDARMERIES, AND CONTINUED TO BE A THORN IN THE SIDE OF THE PEACEKEEPING FORCES.

*THE CITY NOW KNOWN AS LUBUMBASHI

*WAR CRY OF THE GORKHA REGIMENT

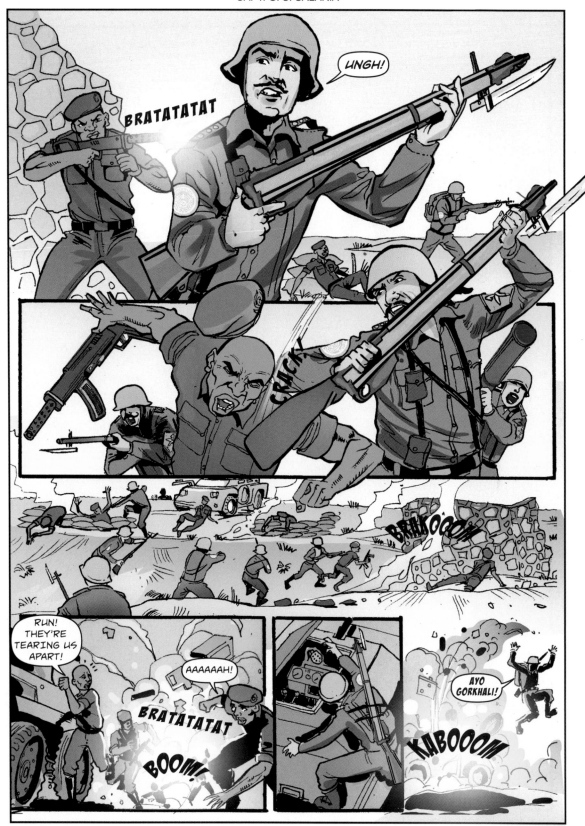

MAJOR DHAN SINGH THAPA

IN OCTOBER, 1962, A WAR BEGAN BETWEEN INDIA AND CHINA OVER LAND ON THE HIMALAYAN BORDER. THE CHINESE FORCES ADVANCED TOWARDS INDIA OVER A LARGE AREA, COVERING AKSAI CHIN AND THE MCMAHON LINE.

EVENTUALLY, A CEASEFIRE WAS DECLARED AND THE WAR ENDED ON 20 NOVEMBER, 1962. CHINA GAINED THE UPPER HAND BUT BOTH SIDES SUFFERED HEAVY CASUALTIES.

AGAINST THE LARGER AND BETTER-EQUIPPED CHINESE ARMY, THE INDIAN TROOPS HAD BEEN AT A SEVERE DISADVANTAGE. HOWEVER, INDIAN SOLDIERS FOUGHT WITH UNPARALLELED COURAGE AND SPIRIT, AND SEVERAL HEROES EMERGED FROM THE RANKS. MAJOR DHAN SINGH THAPA WAS ONE SUCH WAR HERO.

21 OCTOBER, 1962, TOKUNG:

BAD NEWS, SIR. DHAN SINGH THAPA AND ALL 28 MEN WITH HIM ARE REPORTED KILLED IN ACTION.

THE MESSAGE SENT A WAVE OF GLOOM THROUGH THE MEN AT THE POST.

ON 28 AUGUST, 1949, DHAN SINGH THAPA WAS COMMISSIONED INTO 8TH GORKHA RIFLES, A GORKHA REGIMENT OF THE INDIAN ARMY. HE WAS 21 YEARS OLD.

WHEN THE INDO-CHINA WAR BEGAN IN 1962, SIRIJAP VALLEY IN LADAKH BECAME AN IMPORTANT STRATEGIC POINT FOR THE INDIAN ARMY. PLANS HAD TO BE MADE TO PROTECT IT.

I WANT DEFENSIVE OUTPOSTS ALL ALONG THE VALLEY. ANY CHINESE ENCROACHMENT MUST BE THWARTED IMMEDIATELY.

PANGONG LAKE
SIRIJAP VALLEY
CHUSHUL AIRSTRIP

DEFENDING THE VALLEY, WHICH WAS JUST NORTH OF PANGONG LAKE, WAS IMPORTANT FOR THE PROTECTION OF THE CHUSHUL AIRFIELD.

SO, IN OCTOBER, 1962, THE BATTALION 1/8 GORKHA RIFLES WAS SENT TO ESTABLISH OUTPOSTS IN SIRIJAP VALLEY.

MAJOR THAPA WAS COMMANDING A PLATOON THAT HELD A FORWARD POST, SIRIJAP-1.

START DIGGING TRENCHES, BOYS. THE CHINESE MAY ATTACK AT ANY MOMENT.

20 OCTOBER, 1962, 0600 HRS: THE DAY WAS JUST DAWNING, WHEN ALL OF A SUDDEN –

THE POST IS UNDER FIRE!

AS EXPECTED, THE CHINESE ATTACK HAD BEGUN.

THE ASSAULT LASTED TWO AND A HALF HOURS.

THE SHOOTING IS SUBSIDING.

THE WHOLE POST IS ON FIRE!

CALL FOR REINFORCEMENTS. WE MAY NEED THEM.

THE WIRELESS SET IS DAMAGED, SIR.

MAJOR THAPA ADDRESSED HIS MEN.

THE WIRELESS IS OUT. BUT USE ALL YOUR WEAPONRY AND YOUR COURAGE – WE WILL GET BY!

HE BEGAN TO SCOPE OUT THE AREA BEYOND THE TREE LINE.

THERE'S DEFINITELY SOME MOVEMENT THERE.

THEY WILL ATTACK AGAIN.

MAJOR THAPA HAD GAUGED CORRECTLY.

THE FIRING HAS BEGUN AGAIN.

THIS TIME, THOUGH, THE INDIAN SOLDIERS WERE READY.

FIRE!

YAAAAAA!

...THAT THE CHINESE TROOPS SCATTERED.

RETREAT! RETREAT!

THEY LET LOOSE A COUNTER ATTACK SO STRONG...

BUT THE JOY OF THE INDIAN SIDE WOULD BE SHORT-LIVED.

SUFFERING HEAVY CASUALTIES ONLY MADE THE CHINESE MORE DETERMINED.

CALL FOR ADDITIONAL TROOPS. WE'RE LAUNCHING ANOTHER ATTACK.

YOU PROVIDE COVER FIRE. THE REST OF YOU MOVE CLOSER TO THE TARGET.

THE CHINESE ARMY WAS ANGRY AND FRUSTRATED.

WE HAVE LOST SO MANY MEN! HOW COULD WE NOT ANTICIPATE SUCH A TOUGH COUNTER-ATTACK?

THE CHINESE ARMY HAD TO ENSURE NEVER TO UNDERESTIMATE THEIR ENEMY AGAIN.

SO WHEN THE CHINESE SOLDIERS LAUNCHED A THIRD ATTACK, THEIR INFANTRY WAS NOT ADVANCING ALONE.

WHA....?

THEY'VE BROUGHT IN TANKS!

HA, WE HAVE SCARED THEM! KEEP GOING, BOYS.

EVEN AS HE SAID THIS, MAJOR THAPA REALISED THE FRAGILITY OF THEIR POSITION.

WE HAVE LOST TOO MANY MEN, AND OUR AMMUNITION IS RUNNING OUT. HOW WILL WE TAKE ON SUCH A LARGE ARMY?

HOLD OUT FOR AS LONG AS WE HAVE AMMO!

ALTHOUGH THE INDIAN SOLDIERS STUCK TO THAT COMMAND, IT DID NOT TAKE THE CHINESE TOO LONG TO OVERRUN SIRIJAP-1.

AND SO –

BAD NEWS, SIR. DHAN SINGH THAPA AND ALL 28 MEN WITH HIM ARE REPORTED KILLED IN ACTION.

IT IS ALSO REPORTED THAT CHINESE CASUALTIES WERE THREE TIMES THAT NUMBER.

MAJOR THAPA WAS RECOMMENDED FOR THE PARAM VIR CHAKRA.

IN MAY 1963, MUCH TO THE RELIEF AND JOY OF ALL HIS RELATIVES AND FRIENDS –

AMONGST THE INDIAN PRISONERS OF WAR RELEASED BY THE CHINESE ARMY, IS MAJOR DHAN SINGH THAPA....

MAJOR THAPA HAD NOT BEEN KILLED! HE HAD BEEN TAKEN PRISONER OF WAR.

AFTER HIS RELEASE, MAJOR THAPA WAS AWARDED THE PARAM VIR CHAKRA.

....MAJOR THAPA'S COOL COURAGE, CONSPICUOUS FIGHTING QUALITIES AND LEADERSHIP....

MAJOR THAPA RESUMED HIS POSITION AS AN OFFICER OF THE INDIAN ARMY. HE RETIRED AS LT COL DHAN SINGH THAPA IN 1980. THE BRAVE SOLDIER PASSED AWAY IN 2005.

SUBEDAR JOGINDER SINGH

IT WAS A COLD WINTER IN 1962 WHEN SUBEDAR JOGINDER SINGH WAS COMMANDING A PLATOON OF 1 SIKH BATTALION IN THE TAWANG SECTOR OF N.E.F.A.*

SIR, OUR TROOPS HAVE SPOTTED SOME ACTIVITY ACROSS THE BORDER.

WHAT KIND OF ACTIVITY, SOLDIER?

IT APPEARS THAT THE CHINESE ARMY IS ASSEMBLING THERE IN HEAVY NUMBERS, SIR.

THAT CAN'T BE! ARE YOU SURE ABOUT THIS?

EVEN THOUGH THERE HAD BEEN PEACE IN THE REGION, TENSIONS WERE HIGH AS CHINA HAD BEEN STAKING ITS CLAIM OVER CERTAIN AREAS THAT CAME UNDER INDIAN TERRITORY.

RECRUITED IN THE ARMY DURING THE 1930S, 42-YEAR-OLD JOGINDER SINGH WAS DUE TO RETIRE BY THE END OF THE YEAR.

YOU WERE RIGHT! THE CONCENTRATION OF CHINESE SOLDIERS DOES SEEM TO HAVE INCREASED.

JUST A FEW DAYS EARLIER, JOGINDER HAD BEEN SUMMONED BY HIS SENIOR OFFICER.

WE HAVE SUFFERED HEAVY LOSSES IN OTHER AREAS, BUT WE STILL HAVE CONTROL OVER TAWANG. THAT'S THE SECTOR THE CHINESE WANT MOST!

*NORTH-EAST FRONTIER AGENCY, NOW KNOWN AS THE STATE OF ARUNACHAL PRADESH

THE ENEMY IS ADVANCING TOWARDS THE BUM LA FOOT TRACK. THAT'S THE SHORTEST APPROACH TO TAWANG.

YOUR PLATOON WILL GO TO TONGPENG LA AND STOP THIS ADVANCE. IS THAT CLEAR?

YES, SIR!

THE PLATOON OF 1 SIKH BATTALION MADE THE TORTUROUS CLIMB UP TO THE RIDGE AT TONGPENG LA, BATTLING THE ELEMENTS AT OVER 4,400M ABOVE SEA LEVEL.

ONCE AT THE SITE, JOGINDER STUDIED THE AREA AND FIGURED OUT STRATEGIC POINTS OF DEFENCE FOR HIS TROOPS.

WE CAN USE THE RIDGES AND BOULDERS AS BARRIERS TO SHIELD OURSELVES.

THE CHINESE HAVE ALREADY CAUSED HEAVY LOSSES TO US IN OTHER REGIONS. THEY WILL ATTACK HERE NEXT.

IT DID NOT TAKE LONG FOR THE CHINESE ARMY TO MAKE THEIR MOVE. THEY ATTACKED ON 23 OCTOBER, 1962, AT THE FIRST SIGHT OF DAYBREAK.

ARGH!

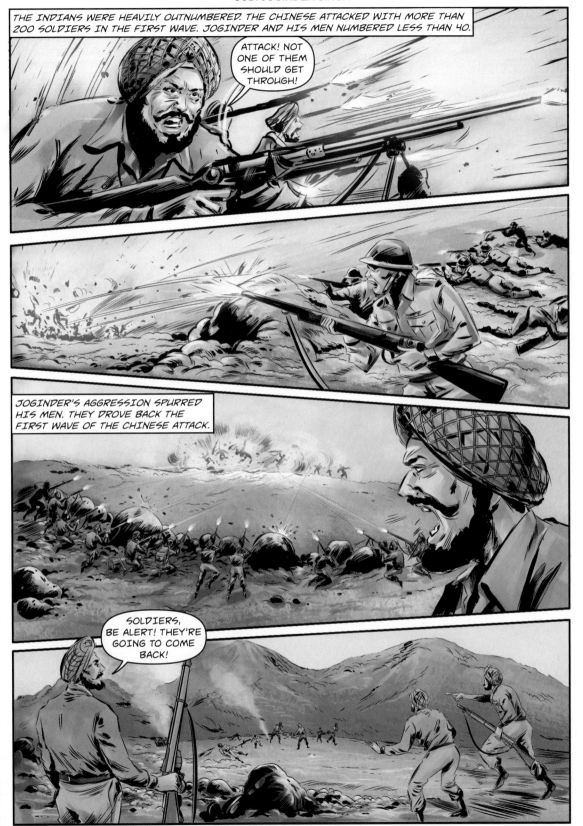

THE INDIANS WERE HEAVILY OUTNUMBERED. THE CHINESE ATTACKED WITH MORE THAN 200 SOLDIERS IN THE FIRST WAVE. JOGINDER AND HIS MEN NUMBERED LESS THAN 40.

ATTACK! NOT ONE OF THEM SHOULD GET THROUGH!

JOGINDER'S AGGRESSION SPURRED HIS MEN. THEY DROVE BACK THE FIRST WAVE OF THE CHINESE ATTACK.

SOLDIERS, BE ALERT! THEY'RE GOING TO COME BACK!

*LIGHT MACHINE GUN

BY THE TIME HE RAN OUT OF AMMUNITION, JOGINDER HAD TAKEN OUT 52 ENEMY SOLDIERS BY HIMSELF. UNFORTUNATELY –

THEY'RE STILL COMING AT US!

FIGHT TILL YOUR LAST BREATH!

THE SOLDIERS KNEW WHAT THEY HAD TO DO. THEY FIXED THEIR BAYONETS AND CHARGED AT THE ENEMY.

WAHE GURUJI DA KHALSA, WAHE GURUJI DI FATEH!*

*BATTLE CRY OF THE SIKH REGIMENT

THE CHINESE SOLDIERS OUTNUMBERED THE INDIANS, AND WON THE BATTLE EVENTUALLY. BUT NOT BEFORE JOGINDER AND HIS MEN TOOK THE LIVES OF MANY MORE OF THEM THROUGH SHEER WILL AND COURAGE.

SUBEDAR JOGINDER SINGH WAS TAKEN CAPTIVE AND DIED AS A PRISONER OF WAR. HE WAS AWARDED THE PARAM VIR CHAKRA POSTHUMOUSLY FOR HIS INSPIRING LEADERSHIP AND BRAVERY OF THE HIGHEST ORDER.

A STATUE COMMEMORATING THIS BRAVE SOLDIER STANDS AS AN INSPIRATION TO ALL IN HIS HOMETOWN OF MOGA.

MAJOR SHAITAN SINGH

"HOW CAN MAN DIE BETTER THAN FACING FEARFUL ODDS FOR THE ASHES OF HIS FATHERS AND THE TEMPLES OF HIS GODS?"

THESE LINES, FROM BRITISH POET THOMAS MACAULAY'S 'LAYS OF ANCIENT ROME', ARE SET IN STONE ON A MEMORIAL GROUND AMIDST THE MOUNTAINS OF JAMMU & KASHMIR.

THE MEMORIAL IS DEDICATED TO THE SOLDIERS OF 13 KUMAON REGIMENT, WHO FOUGHT IN THE BATTLE OF REZANG LA, UNDER THE LEADERSHIP OF MAJOR SHAITAN SINGH.

SHAITAN SINGH WAS BORN ON 1 DECEMBER, 1924, IN BANASAR, A VILLAGE IN JODHPUR, RAJASTHAN. THE VILLAGE HAS SINCE BEEN RENAMED SHAITAN SINGH NAGAR.

JODHPUR SAW HIM GROW UP FROM A SERIOUS, SOFT-SPOKEN CHILD INTO AN UPRIGHT AND CONFIDENT GRADUATE OF JASWANT COLLEGE.

IN 1946, SHAITAN SINGH, ALONG WITH SOME FRIENDS, WAS SELECTED AS A CADET FOR JODHPUR LANCERS.

CONGRATULATIONS!

TO YOU TOO! YOU HAVE BIG SHOES TO FILL, SHAITAN!

WHY?

SHAITAN'S FATHER WAS IN THE JODHPUR LANCERS TOO. LT COL HEM SINGHJI SIR FOUGHT IN THE FIRST WORLD WAR.

REALLY?

YES. HE WAS GIVEN AN O.B.E.* FOR BRAVERY AND DEVOTION TO DUTY!

WITH SUCH A STRONG ROLE MODEL, SHAITAN SINGH SURPRISED NO ONE WHEN HE BECAME AN EXEMPLARY SOLDIER. IN 1949, WHEN MAHARAJA HANWANT SINGH OF JODHPUR ACCEDED TO THE GOVERNMENT OF INDEPENDENT INDIA, HE WAS SELECTED TO JOIN THE KUMAON REGIMENT OF THE INDIAN ARMY.

*ORDER OF THE BRITISH EMPIRE

AFTER BECOMING CAPTAIN IN 1955, HE WAS PART OF THE 1961 LIBERATION OF GOA, A BATTLE WHERE THE INDIAN ARMED FORCES ENSURED THE END OF PORTUGUESE RULE IN INDIA.

CAPTAIN, WE ARE VERY HAPPY WITH YOUR PERFORMANCE IN THE GOA OPERATIONS. YOUR STRONG SENSE OF DUTY SETS A VERY GOOD EXAMPLE.

THANK YOU, SIR.

A YEAR LATER, INDIA WAS INVOLVED WITH CHINA IN A WAR OVER DISPUTED TERRITORY ALONG THE HIMALAYAS.

OUR COUNTRY NEEDS ALL HANDS ON DECK. ALL REGIMENTS MUST BE DEPLOYED IMMEDIATELY.

13 KUMAON REGIMENT WAS DEPLOYED, AND SHAITAN SINGH, NOW A MAJOR, COMMANDED THE 123 MEN OF THE CHARLIE COMPANY WHO WERE STATIONED AT REZANG LA*.

ALMOST 18,000FT HIGH, THE CHARLIE COMPANY BEGAN BUILDING POSTS AND BUNKERS IN THE MOUNTAINS.

BRRR..I DIDN'T REALISE IT'D BE SO COLD.

DON'T TAKE BREAKS. THE WORK KEEPS THE BODY WARM.

*A PASS NEAR CHUSHUL VALLEY IN LADAKH

99

BUT AS SHAITAN SINGH APPROACHED THE BUNKER –

WHCK!

WITH THE LOSS OF EACH OF OUR SOLDIERS, THE ODDS ARE GETTING STACKED HIGHER AGAINST US. BUT I MUST MAKE SURE THEY DON'T GET DISHEARTENED.

MAKE ARRANGEMENTS TO EVACUATE MAJOR SA'AB. HE'S INJURED.

YES, I'M ON IT.

NO NEED FOR THAT. I'LL BE FINE... JUST GIVE ME THE FIRST AID KIT.

BY THE TIME THE NEXT CHINESE ATTACK CAME, CHARLIE COMPANY HAD LOST SEVERAL MEN. BUT FOR EVERY INDIAN SOLDIER WHO LOST HIS LIFE, THERE HAD BEEN ALMOST SEVEN CHINESE CASUALTIES.

THE CHINESE WAVE TACTICS WERE AIMED AT INTIMIDATING AND DISINTEGRATING THE INDIANS BY THE SHEER STRENGTH OF THEIR NUMBERS. ALTHOUGH THEY WERE ADVERSELY OUTNUMBERED, THE FEARLESS GROUP OF INDIAN SOLDIERS REFUSED TO YIELD.

REZANG LA WILL SOON BE OVERRUN WITH CHINESE SOLDIERS. GO TO THE BASE. INFORM THEM OF THE SITUATION HERE AND HOW WE'VE FOUGHT.

I'LL STAY BACK. I'VE STILL GOT SOME FIGHT LEFT IN ME!

BUT SIR...

THAT'S AN ORDER.

WITH THAT, SHAITAN SINGH AND THE REST OF HIS MEN TURNED TO FACE THE ENEMY ONCE AGAIN.

THIS WAS SHAITAN SINGH'S FINAL STAND. HE HAD INSPIRED HIS MEN TO KEEP GOING AGAINST IMPOSSIBLE ODDS. EACH OF THEM FOUGHT TILL THE LAST BULLET.

FOR PLACING HIS DUTY ABOVE HIS PERSONAL SAFETY AND FOR HIS FEARLESS LEADERSHIP, MAJOR SHAITAN SINGH WAS POSTHUMOUSLY AWARDED THE PARAM VIR CHAKRA.

114 INDIAN SOLDIERS DIED THAT DAY BUT THEY TOOK DOWN OVER 1300 ENEMY SOLDIERS, DELIVERING A STAGGERING BLOW TO THE CHINESE ARMY.

THREE MONTHS AFTER THE BATTLE OF REZANG LA, THE ARMY SENT A DELEGATION TO RECOVER THE BODIES OF THE BRAVE SOLDIERS. AMIDST THE TRAGIC AFTERMATH OF THE BATTLE, WHAT STRUCK THEM MOST WAS THAT THE INDIAN SOLDIERS HAD ALL DIED FACING THE ENEMY, WEAPONS IN HAND.

CQMH* ABDUL HAMID

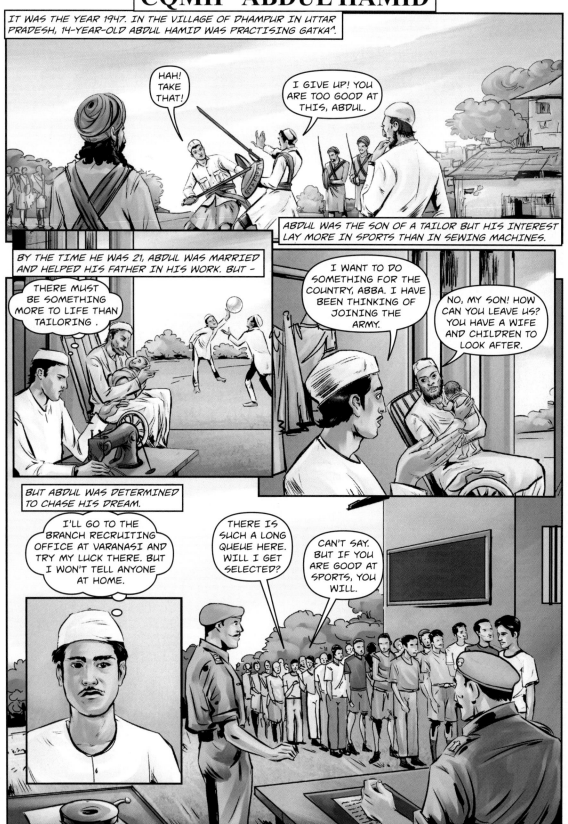

IT WAS THE YEAR 1947. IN THE VILLAGE OF DHAMPUR IN UTTAR PRADESH, 14-YEAR-OLD ABDUL HAMID WAS PRACTISING GATKA^.

HAH! TAKE THAT!

I GIVE UP! YOU ARE TOO GOOD AT THIS, ABDUL.

ABDUL WAS THE SON OF A TAILOR BUT HIS INTEREST LAY MORE IN SPORTS THAN IN SEWING MACHINES.

BY THE TIME HE WAS 21, ABDUL WAS MARRIED AND HELPED HIS FATHER IN HIS WORK. BUT –

THERE MUST BE SOMETHING MORE TO LIFE THAN TAILORING.

I WANT TO DO SOMETHING FOR THE COUNTRY, ABBA. I HAVE BEEN THINKING OF JOINING THE ARMY.

NO, MY SON! HOW CAN YOU LEAVE US? YOU HAVE A WIFE AND CHILDREN TO LOOK AFTER.

BUT ABDUL WAS DETERMINED TO CHASE HIS DREAM.

I'LL GO TO THE BRANCH RECRUITING OFFICE AT VARANASI AND TRY MY LUCK THERE. BUT I WON'T TELL ANYONE AT HOME.

THERE IS SUCH A LONG QUEUE HERE. WILL I GET SELECTED?

CAN'T SAY. BUT IF YOU ARE GOOD AT SPORTS, YOU WILL.

*COMPANY QUARTER MASTER HAVILDAR

^AN INDIAN MARTIAL ART IN WHICH A WOODEN STICK IS USED TO SIMULATE SWORD FIGHTING

AFTER HIS TRAINING, ABDUL HAMID JOINED 4TH BATTALION, THE GRENADIERS, AN INFANTRY REGIMENT OF THE INDIAN ARMY. HE REMAINED WITH THE SAME BATTALION ALL HIS SERVICE LIFE.

IN 1962, HE TOOK PART IN THE INDO-CHINA WAR. AFTER THAT HE WAS PROMOTED TO CQMH. DURING THIS PERIOD, ABDUL WAS AWARDED THREE SERVICE MEDALS – THE SAINYA SEVA MEDAL, THE SAMAR SEVA MEDAL AND THE RAKSHA MEDAL.

IN 1965, WAR BROKE OUT BETWEEN INDIA AND PAKISTAN. THE COMPANY COMMANDER ADDRESSED THE MEN OF THE BATTALION.

INTELLIGENCE REPORTS TELL US THAT THE ENEMY PLANS TO LAUNCH HEAVY ARTILLERY AND TANK ATTACKS ON OUR COMMUNICATION AND SUPPLY ROUTES IN JAMMU & KASHMIR.

OUR BATTALION HAS BEEN DETAILED TO MOVE TO CHIMA VILLAGE. THE AREA IS COVERED WITH ONION AND SUGARCANE FIELDS AND IS ON THE KHEM KARAN-BHIKIWIND ROAD.

ABDUL HAMID! AS OUR BEST RIFLE SHOT, YOU WILL BE IN CHARGE OF OUR ANTI-TANK CREW. YOU WILL COMMAND A RECOILLESS GUN DETACHMENT.

SIR!

GET READY TO LEAVE IMMEDIATELY!

THE BATTALION WAS SOON ON ITS WAY.

THERE ARE THE SUGARCANE FIELDS!

ON REACHING THEIR POSITION, THE MEN DUG TRENCHES WHILE HAMID AND HIS CREW CAMOUFLAGED THEIR ANTI-TANK JEEP.

ON 10 SEPTEMBER, 1965, AT 0600 HRS, THE PAKISTANI ARMY BEGAN INTENSE SHELLING ON THE BATTALION.

BY 0900 HRS —

THEY ARE SENDING IN PATTON TANKS!

ABDUL AND HIS DRIVER SPRINTED TO THEIR JEEP.

AS THE DRIVER DROVE THE VEHICLE OUT OF ITS HIDING PLACE...

...ABDUL LEAPT IN. THEY HAD TO STOP THE ENEMY TANKS.

ABDUL HAMID POSITIONED HIS GUN AND –

TAKE THAT...

...AND THAT!

YES!
IT'S A HAT
TRICK!

BY THIS TIME, THE ENEMY WAS DETERMINED NOT TO
LET HIM GET AWAY.

HE'S GOT
THREE OF OUR
TANKS! GET HIM!
HE IS ALONE AND
UNABLE TO MOVE
WITHOUT A
DRIVER.

I HAVE TO GET THEM!

BEFORE HAMID COULD FIRE ON THE FOURTH PATTON TANK, HE WAS HIT.

AAAAAAH!

THE GALLANT SOLDIER DIED ON THE SPOT.

INSPIRED BY THEIR COMRADE, THE MEN OF 4 GRENADIERS BEAT BACK THE HEAVY TANK ASSAULT.

भारत INDIA

3.00

भारत गणराज्य के 50 वर्ष
50 YEARS OF THE REPUBLIC OF INDIA

FOR HIS ACT OF EXTREME COURAGE, ABDUL HAMID WAS AWARDED THE PARAM VIR CHAKRA, POSTHUMOUSLY.

LT COL ARDESHIR BURZORJI TARAPORE

ON 1 JANUARY, 1942, ARDESHIR BURZORJI TARAPORE WAS COMMISSIONED TO THE 7TH HYDERABAD INFANTRY OF THE HYDERABAD STATE FORCES.

I REALLY WISH I COULD RIDE A SCOUT CAR*! TOO BAD THE INFANTRY CAN'T USE THEM.

TARAPORE DEARLY WANTED TO BE PART OF THE ARMOURED REGIMENT.

THEN ONE DAY, DURING A TRAINING EXERCISE AT THE GRENADE-THROWING RANGE –

HIGHER! PUT YOUR WEIGHT INTO IT.

OH!

TARAPORE, BE CAREFUL.

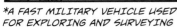

*A FAST MILITARY VEHICLE USED FOR EXPLORING AND SURVEYING

TARAPORE HAD TAKEN A SPRAY OF SHRAPNEL TO HIS CHEST.

GET A MEDIC, QUICK!

UNBEKNOWN TO THE GROUP, THE INCIDENT WAS WITNESSED BY THE COMMANDER-IN-CHIEF, GENERAL EL-EDROOS.

WHO'S THAT YOUNG GENTLEMAN?

ONE OF OUR INFANTRY OFFICERS, SIR. TARAPORE.

AFTER TARAPORE HAD RECOVERED, GENERAL EDROOS CALLED HIM TO HIS OFFICE.

YOU WERE VERY BRAVE YESTERDAY. WELL DONE!

THANK YOU, SIR.

YOU SHOWED GREAT PRESENCE OF MIND. IS THERE ANYTHING WE CAN DO FOR YOU?

MAY I MAKE A REQUEST, SIR?

GENERAL EDROOS GRANTED TARAPORE'S WISH TO BE TRANSFERRED TO THE ARMOURED REGIMENT, 1ST HYDERABAD IMPERIAL SERVICE LANCERS.

AT HIS NEW REGIMENT, TARAPORE HAD A COMMANDING OFFICER WHO WAS DISMISSIVE OF SOLDIERS FROM INDIA.

INDIAN SOLDIERS DO NOT SHOW TRUE BRAVERY. YOU'RE NOT UP TO THE MARK.

THIS LED TO FRICTION BETWEEN HIM AND TARAPORE, WHO ALWAYS SPOKE UP AGAINST UNFAIRNESS.

UNTIL 1948, THE NIZAM OF HYDERABAD WISHED FOR HIS STATE TO REMAIN INDEPENDENT. BUT IN 1948, HE RELINQUISHED CONTROL AND HYDERABAD BECAME A STATE OF INDIA. GENERAL EL-EDROOS SURRENDERED TO MAJOR GENERAL CHAUDHURY OF THE INDIAN ARMY.

THE HYDERABAD STATE FORCES ALSO HAD TO BE DISSOLVED AND SOME OF THE OFFICERS WERE TRANSFERRED TO THE INDIAN ARMY.

ON 1 APRIL, 1951, TARAPORE WAS SELECTED TO SERVE THE INDIAN ARMY AND POSTED TO POONA HORSE, AN ARMOURED REGIMENT IN JAMMU. IN THE 'A' SQUADRON OF THE REGIMENT, HE WAS UNDER MAJOR 'BALLI' VIRK.

THIS IS CAPTAIN TARAPORE, EX-HYDERABAD LANCERS. AN EXCELLENT SOLDIER. HE'S JUST JOINED THE REGIMENT.

THANK YOU, SIR. GOOD AFTERNOON.

IT WAS HERE THAT THE YOUNG SOLDIER TRULY CAME INTO HIS OWN.

LET'S GET YOU SETTLED IN, ADI.

ABSOLUTELY, SIR. NICE TO MEET YOU ALL.

SOME OF THE OFFICERS WERE COMPLAINING ABOUT CAPTAIN TARAPORE JOINING US. EX-ENEMY, THEY CALLED HIM.

HYDERABAD STATE IS PART OF THE UNION OF INDIA NOW. HE SEEMS LIKE A SMART OFFICER. I'M SURE HE'LL BE A GOOD FIT.

WITH TIME, CAPTAIN TARAPORE'S FRIENDLY AND SENSITIVE NATURE GOT RID OF ALL APPREHENSIONS.

SHIVJEE, WHAT'S WRONG?

LIEUTENANT SHIVRAJ SINGH WAS ONE OF HIS CLOSEST FRIENDS IN THE REGIMENT. THE TWO, ALONG WITH MAJOR BALLI, THE SQUADRON COMMANDER, MADE A GREAT TEAM.

NOTHING, SIR.

TELL ME. SHARING YOUR TROUBLES MAY LIGHTEN YOUR HEART.

ADI SIR ALWAYS HAS TIME FOR HIS FRIENDS. HE IS SUCH A WONDERFUL PERSON.

MY UNCLE PASSED AWAY....

I'M SORRY.

TARAPORE WAS A MAN WHO TOOK SWIFT DECISIONS. IN 1962, HE WAS OFFICIATING AS COMMANDANT, WHEN —

I'VE JUST RECEIVED ORDERS THAT OUR REGIMENT HAS TO MOVE ITS OPERATIONAL BASE IN 24 HRS.

BUT ADI SIR, IT TAKES ABOUT TWO DAYS JUST TO GET THE CLEARANCE FROM....

FORGET THE CLEARANCE. WE NEED TO MOVE QUICKLY. NIRANJANJI AND VEERUJI, GET YOUR MEN TO BREAK THE SECURITY FENCING AROUND THE QUARTER GUARD AND THE AMMUNITION DUMP. WE'LL TAKE THE TANKS RIGHT UP TO THE AMMUNITION BAYS AND LOAD THEM.

THE M.E.S.* WILL RAISE DAMAGE REPORTS.

YES, THEY WILL. LATER. AND THAT'S WHEN I'LL SORT THEM OUT — AFTER WE'VE MOVED.

LET'S GET TO WORK.

THE REGIMENT WORKED THROUGH THE NIGHT AND WAS ABLE TO MOVE ON SCHEDULE.

*MILITARY ENGINEERING SERVICES

THERE WAS A FUN SIDE TO TARAPORE AS WELL – ONE THAT HIS FRIENDS LOVED.

ONE EVENING, AFTER A FEW DRINKS –

I AM NAPOLEON, REINCARNATED!

YOU NEED A HAT!

A HAT! YOU'RE RIGHT... AHA!

HA HA HA

IF YOU WANT A THING DONE WELL....

A.B TARAPORE

IN AUGUST, 1965, WAR BROKE OUT BETWEEN INDIA AND PAKISTAN. THE FIGHTING WAS INTENSE AND THE ARMED FORCES FULLY INVOLVED. THE FIERCEST TANK BATTLE TOOK PLACE IN PHILLORA, SIALKOT.

TO CAPTURE PHILLORA, THE INDIAN ARMY DECIDED TO LAUNCH AN ATTACK FROM THE SOUTH. ON 11 SEPTEMBER, 1965 –

....TO GET TO PHILLORA. TARAPORE, YOUR REGIMENT WILL DELIVER THE MAIN ARMOURED THRUST FROM THE RIGHT FLANK.

SIR!

AT THE TIME, LIEUTENANT COLONEL TARAPORE WAS COMMANDING THE 17 HORSE REGIMENT.

THE ATTACK WAS PLANNED –

WE'LL LAUNCH A SURPRISE ATTACK FROM THE REAR. WE'LL MOVE AT 0600 HRS PAST KHANAWALI TO PHILLORA.

THE 'C' SQUADRON WILL LEAD, FOLLOWED BY THE REGIMENTAL HQ AND THE 'B' SQUADRON. 'A' SQUADRON WILL BRING UP THE REAR.

BUT BEFORE THEY COULD REACH PHILLORA, THE REGIMENT WAS MET WITH A COUNTERATTACK FROM AN ARMOURED BRIGADE OF THE ENEMY.

LOOKS LIKE PAKISTAN HAS BROUGHT OUT THE BIG GUNS.

'C' SQUADRON HAS RUN INTO TROUBLE. 'B' SQUADRON, GUARD THE NORTH-WEST FLANK.

THE REGIMENT STOOD ITS GROUND, AND DEFIED THE CHARGE WITH THE SUPPORT OF THE INFANTRY BATTALION.

THE ENEMY WAS ROUTED.

LOOKS LIKE WE'RE IN THE CLEAR.

'C' SQUADRON, PROCEED TO PHILLORA.

WHEN THEY HALTED, CAPTAIN GURDIAL SINGH FROM 'A' SQUADRON NOTICED THAT TARAPORE WAS INJURED.

AT PHILLORA, THEY FACED MORE RESISTANCE. BUT THE INDIAN SIDE WAS ORGANISED AND RUTHLESS AND BY THAT AFTERNOON, PHILLORA HAD BEEN CAPTURED.

TARAPORE WAS LEAVING TO CHECK ON ANOTHER SECTOR WHERE HIS REGIMENT WAS FIGHTING, WHEN –

STOP, STOP!

SHIVJEE! HELLO! WHERE ARE YOU OFF TO?

I'M HERE TO EVACUATE YOU. I WAS TOLD C.O. 17 HORSE IS WOUNDED.

WHAT? I'M NOT LEAVING THE REGIMENT AND ALL THE FUN BECAUSE OF A LITTLE SCRATCH!

NICE TO SEE YOU, SHIVJEE. WE SHOULD CATCH UP ONCE THIS IS OVER.

AND WITH THAT, HE HEADED OFF.

ON 16 SEPTEMBER, THE REGIMENT CAPTURED JASSORAN AND BUTUR-DOGRANDI. THEY ESTABLISHED PIVOTS AT THESE PLACES AND WERE SET TO MOVE, WHEN –

SIR, THERE IS A MESSAGE FROM CHAWINDA. THE ENEMY IS FLEEING. IT IS A GOOD TIME TO ATTACK.

LET'S GO JOIN THEM, ADJUTANT.

TARAPORE MOVED THE TANKS SWIFTLY TO CHAWINDA...

...WHERE THEY ENGAGED IN A FIERCE BATTLE WITH A DESPERATE ENEMY.

JUST THEN –

WHUMP!

WE'VE BEEN HIT. I AM GOING OUT TO CHECK.

BE CAREFUL, SIR.

AS TARAPORE JUMPED OUT TO ASSESS THE DAMAGE, HIS RADIO OFFICER FOLLOWED HIM.

AHH!

A BULLET CAUGHT THE YOUNG OFFICER JUST AS HE STEPPED OUT.

HOISTING HIS INJURED COMPANION ON HIS SHOULDER, TARAPORE MADE A DASH TO SAFETY...

...BUT WAS SOON BACK TO CONTINUE THE BATTLE.

THE BATTLE OF CHAWINDA WAS ONE OF THE LARGEST TANK BATTLES IN WORLD HISTORY AND INDIA HAD THE UPPER HAND. 60 PAKISTANI TANKS WERE DECIMATED WHILE INDIA LOST ONLY NINE.

BUT ONE OF THESE CASUALTIES WAS LT COL TARAPORE'S TANK.

....FROM THE LEFT AND I'LL BE IN... HUH!

BHOOSHH!

IT RECEIVED A DIRECT HIT.

UNDER TARAPORE'S COMMAND, THE POONA HORSE REGIMENT PERFORMED EXCELLENTLY IN THE 1965 WAR.

FOR HIS BRAVERY AND EXCEPTIONAL LEADERSHIP, LT COL ARDESHIR BURZORJI TARAPORE WAS POSTHUMOUSLY AWARDED THE PARAM VIR CHAKRA.

LT COL ADERSHIR TARAPORE DESCENDED FROM RATANJIBA, WHO WAS ONE OF THE MILITARY LEADERS UNDER SHIVAJI. TO REWARD RATANJIBA FOR HIS LOYALTY AND BRAVERY, SHIVAJI HAD GIVEN HIM A MANSAB* OF 100 VILLAGES. THE PREMIER VILLAGE WAS CALLED TARAPUR AND THAT WAS HOW THE TARAPORE FAMILY NAME CAME INTO BEING.

*THE MANSABDARI SYSTEM WAS A SYSTEM OF MILITARY RANKING IN MEDIEVAL INDIA.

LANCE NAIK ALBERT EKKA

I CAN'T WAIT FOR TRAINING TO BE A REAL SOLDIER, ALBERT!

AND I CAN'T WAIT TO FIGHT IN A REAL WAR!

NINE YEARS LATER, IN 1971, LANCE NAIK ALBERT EKKA DID GET TO FIGHT IN A REAL WAR.

EAST PAKISTAN IS STRUGGLING TO GAIN FREEDOM FROM WEST PAKISTAN.

INDIA WILL SOON BE DRAWN INTO THEIR WAR.

BUT IT'S NOT OUR WAR. WHY SHOULD WE GET INVOLVED IN A DISPUTE BETWEEN OUR NEIGHBOURS?

SOMETIMES WE HAVE TO, WHEN A NEIGHBOUR IS IN TROUBLE.

A FEW DAYS LATER, ON 3 DECEMBER, 1971, PAKISTAN LAUNCHED AN ATTACK ON INDIA'S WESTERN BORDERS.

PAKISTAN HAS ATTACKED 11 OF OUR AIRBASES.

NOW WE WILL GET ORDERS TO MOVE TO THE WAR FRONT!

THE MEN OF 14TH GUARDS WERE GIVEN THEIR FIRST MISSION AND ASKED TO MOVE TO GANGASAGAR* ON THE EASTERN FRONT.

WE HAVE TO CAPTURE AKHAURA^. TO REACH THERE, WE HAVE TO DRIVE OUT THE ENEMY FROM THEIR BUNKERS IN GANGASAGAR.

OUR ROUTE LIES ALONG A RAILWAY LINE WHERE THERE IS NO COVER. WE HAVE TO CLOSE IN AND ATTACK WITH GRENADES AND BAYONETS.

*GANGASAGAR IS IN AGARTALA

^AKHAURA IS NOW IN BANGLADESH ON THE BORDER NEAR AGARTALA

ALBERT WAS PART OF THE LEFT FORWARD COMPANY OF THE BATTALION WHICH WENT IN FOR THE FIRST ATTACK.

KEEP IN A SINGLE FILE AND BEND LOW.

AN ASSAULT GROUP WAS FORMED TO BREAK INTO THE ENEMY LINES. ALBERT WAS PART OF IT.

KEEP MOVING!

CAREFUL!

SUDDENLY, THEY WERE FACED WITH A BARRAGE OF FIRING.

THE FIRING IS COMING FROM AN L.M.G. IN THAT BUNKER. WE MUST STOP IT! GET READY TO ATTACK WHEN I GIVE THE ORDER TO CHARGE!

A SOLDIER NEXT TO ALBERT COLLAPSED TO THE GROUND.

THE SMOKE... IT IS CHOKING ME!

HANG ON! WE WILL CHARGE IN A MINUTE!

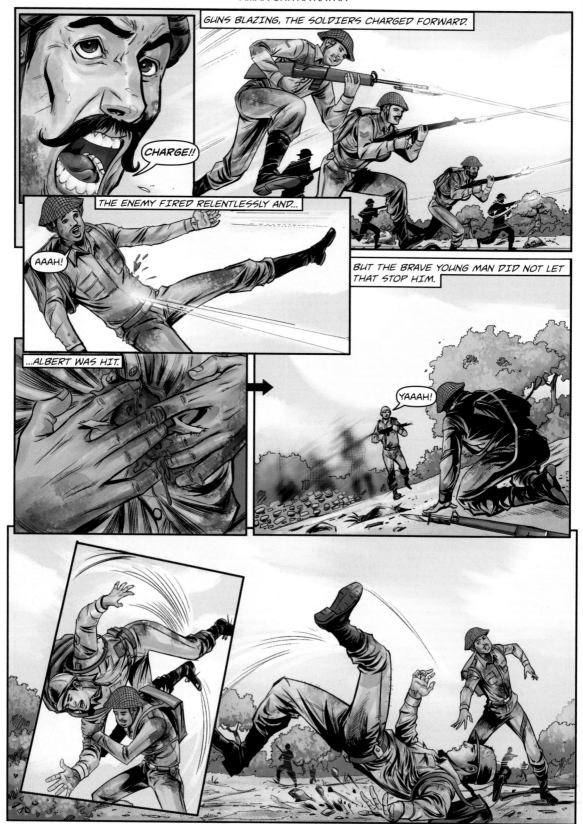

LOOMING UP IN FRONT OF HIM WAS THE COMPOUND WALL OF THE BUILDING.

I CANNOT CLIMB THE WALL. THE ENEMY WILL SURELY SPOT ME. I WILL HAVE TO LEAP OVER IT IN ONE SWIFT MOVE.

ALBERT MEASURED HIS RUN-UP TO THE WALL AND –

UNGF!

PUSHING HIS WEAKENED BODY, ALBERT DASHED IN.

THEY HAVEN'T SEEN ME YET.

IN A SWIFT MOTION, HE SILENCED THE ENEMY SOLDIERS AND THE DEADLY GUN.

WITH THE GUN SILENCED, ALBERT'S COMRADES RAISED A CHEER!

GREAT JOB, EKKA! NOW WE CAN GET ON WITH FORCING THE ENEMY TO VACATE AKHAURA.

ALBERT STAGGERED OUT.

MUST HELP THE BATTALION WRAP UP OPERATIONS.

BUT HIS INJURIES HAD TAKEN A HEAVY TOLL.

AAH!

ALBERT!

HE'S GONE!

BARELY TWO WEEKS LATER, ON 16 DECEMBER, 1971, PAKISTAN SURRENDERED.

ALBERT EKKA DID NOT LIVE TO SEE THE VICTORY OF THE ALLIED FORCES OF INDIA AND BANGLADESH OVER PAKISTAN. BUT HIS SIGNIFICANT ROLE HAS BEEN RECOGNISED.

IN JANUARY, 1972 –

IN THIS ACTION, LANCE NAIK ALBERT EKKA DISPLAYED THE MOST CONSPICUOUS VALOUR AND DETERMINATION....

IN 2000, ON OUR 50TH REPUBLIC DAY, THE INDIAN GOVERNMENT ISSUED A POSTAL STAMP IN ALBERT'S MEMORY.

INDIA
300

THIS SON OF RANCHI WAS ALSO HONOURED WHEN HIS STATUE WAS INSTALLED AT A MAJOR INTERSECTION IN THE CITY WHICH WAS THEN NAMED THE ALBERT EKKA CHOWK.

FLYING OFFICER NIRMAL JIT SINGH SEKHON

DURING THE 1971 CONFLICT BETWEEN INDIA AND PAKISTAN, AN EVENT ALSO KNOWN AS THE BANGLADESH LIBERATION WAR, WEST PAKISTAN SENT MILITARY TO CRUSH THE MOVEMENT FOR FREEDOM TAKING PLACE IN EAST PAKISTAN.

THIS RESULTED IN UNIMAGINABLE DESTRUCTION AND LARGE SCALE MASSACRE OF INNOCENT PEOPLE.

PEOPLE FLEEING FROM EAST PAKISTAN SOUGHT REFUGE IN INDIA.

IN RESPONSE, THE STATE GOVERNMENTS OF WEST BENGAL, BIHAR, MEGHALAYA, ASSAM AND TRIPURA, SET UP REFUGEE CAMPS ALONG THEIR BORDERS.

SOON, AT AN AIRBASE IN NORTH INDIA –

THE PRIME MINISTER HAS ANNOUNCED THAT WE WILL PROVIDE EAST PAKISTAN WITH MILITARY AID ALSO.

IN RETALIATION TO THIS MOVE, WEST PAKISTAN LAUNCHED AIR STRIKES ON ELEVEN INDIAN AIRBASES IN NORTH WESTERN INDIA ON 3 DECEMBER. THIS BLEW INTO A FULL-SCALE WAR BETWEEN INDIA AND PAKISTAN THAT ENDED WITH PAKISTAN'S UNCONDITIONAL SURRENDER ON 16 DECEMBER, 1971.

NO. 18 SQUADRON OF THE INDIAN AIR FORCE, CALLED 'FLYING BULLETS', WAS CHARGED WITH THE DEFENCE OF THE KASHMIR VALLEY.

A DETACHMENT OF FOUR OF OUR 'FLYING BULLETS' WILL REPORT AT SRINAGAR AIRBASE AT 0600 HRS TOMORROW.

BECAUSE OF AN INTERNATIONAL AGREEMENT MADE IN 1948, DEFENCE AIRCRAFT WERE NOT ALLOWED TO BE STATIONED AT SRINAGAR. SO WHEN THE FIGHTER AIRCRAFT MOVED THERE IN 1971, IT WAS THE FIRST TIME THE AIRCREW AND TECHNICAL PERSONNEL WERE DEALING WITH THE ROUGH TERRAIN AND COLD CLIMATE OF KASHMIR.

DID YOU KNOW IT WOULD BE THIS FREEZING?

NO. I CAN BARELY FEEL MY HANDS!

THE 'FLYING BULLETS' DETACHMENT COMPRISED EIGHT PILOTS, 78 TECHNICAL AND SUPPORT STAFF, BESIDES FOUR FOLLAND GNATS. A LIGHT SUBSONIC FIGHTER AIRCRAFT, THE GNAT WAS DEVELOPED FOR THE UNITED KINGDOM'S ROYAL AIR FORCE AND INDUCTED INTO THE INDIAN AIR FORCE IN 1958.

THE GNAT WAS NICKNAMED 'SABRE SLAYER' BECAUSE OF ITS REPUTATION FROM THE 1965 WAR AGAINST PAKISTAN, WHEN THE TECHNICALLY FAR SUPERIOR PAKISTANI SABRES SUFFERED GREAT LOSSES AT THE HANDS OF THE HUMBLE INDIAN GNATS.

IN DECEMBER, 1971, PAKISTAN PLANNED A MISSION TO ATTACK SRINAGAR AIRBASE WITH A WAVE OF F86 SABRES.

EACH SABRE WAS EQUIPPED WITH TWO 500LB* BOMBS AND 12.7MM GUNS.

AT PESHAWAR AIRBASE OF THE PAKISTAN AIR FORCE (P.A.F.) —

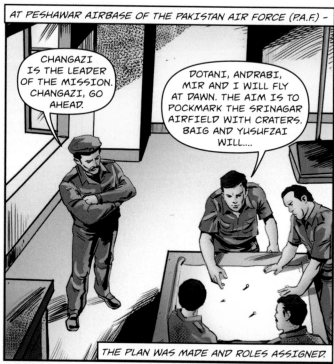

CHANGAZI IS THE LEADER OF THE MISSION. CHANGAZI, GO AHEAD.

DOTANI, ANDRABI, MIR AND I WILL FLY AT DAWN. THE AIM IS TO POCKMARK THE SRINAGAR AIRFIELD WITH CRATERS. BAIG AND YUSUFZAI WILL....

THE PLAN WAS MADE AND ROLES ASSIGNED.

AND SO, ON 14 DECEMBER, A STRIKE FORCE OF FOUR SABRES OF P.A.F'S 26 SQUADRON, NAMED 'BLACK SPIDERS', FLEW EAST TOWARDS SRINAGAR.

AS THEY APPROACHED PIR PANJAL, AN INDIAN OBSERVATION POST DETECTED THEM.

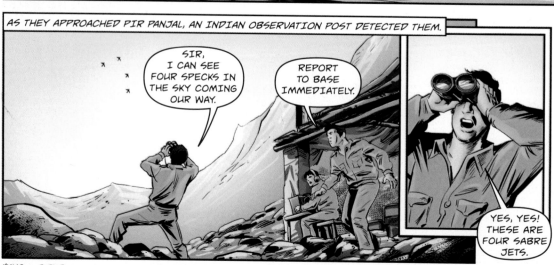

SIR, I CAN SEE FOUR SPECKS IN THE SKY COMING OUR WAY.

REPORT TO BASE IMMEDIATELY.

YES, YES! THESE ARE FOUR SABRE JETS.

*1KG = 2.2LB

IN THE AIR TRAFFIC CONTROL (A.T.C.) TOWER AT THE BASE –

FOUR SABRES ARE FLYING THIS WAY. SCRAMBLE* OUR O.R.P.^ AIRCRAFT.

YES, SIR.

THE PILOTS AT O.R.P. 1 WERE FLT LT GHUMAN AND FG OFFR SEKHON.

IT'S A FOGGY DAY, G MAN**. WE MAY HAVE SOME SLOW HOURS TO LOOK FORWARD TO.

I THINK YOU'RE RIGHT, BROTHER**.

AT 0800 HRS –

TYOOOOON...TYOOOOON...

WITHIN SECONDS, BOTH THE OFFICERS WERE READY FOR TAKE-OFF. BUT, AIR DEFENCE HAD STARTED FIRING ANTI-AIRCRAFT GUNS AT THE INTRUDERS.

IN THE A.T.C. –

WE CAN'T CLEAR THEM FOR TAKE OFF RIGHT NOW. THE GUNNERS ARE ACTIVE AND THEY'RE TOO CLOSE.

*COMMAND GIVEN TO LAUNCH AIRCRAFT FOR COMBAT
^OPERATION READINESS PLATFORM

**BROTHER AND GMAN WERE NICKNAMES GIVEN TO SEKHON AND GHUMAN RESPECTIVELY.

BUT THE TWO PILOTS WERE RARING TO GO.

I CAN'T WAIT FOR A.T.C. CLEARANCE. THE SABRES ARE CLOSING IN NOW.

WITH THAT, FLT LT GHUMAN TOOK OFF.

I'LL HAVE TO WAIT FOR THE DUST TO SETTLE. THE VISIBILITY IS NEAR ZERO.

TWENTY SECONDS LATER, WHEN SEKHON TOOK OFF, TWO PAIRS OF BOMBS EXPLODED ON THE RUNWAY BEHIND HIM.

THE ENEMY AIRCRAFT ARE OVERHEAD!

I CAN SEE A TARGET. I'M IN PURSUIT.

CHANGAZI AND DOTANI, THE PAKISTANI PILOTS, HAD DROPPED THE BOMBS AND FLOWN STRAIGHT INTO SEKHON'S CROSSHAIRS*.

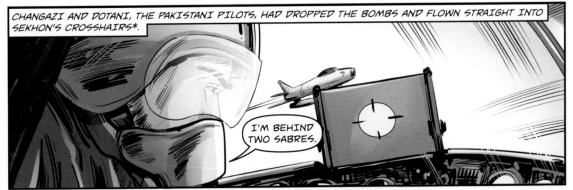

I'M BEHIND TWO SABRES.

THE SABRES SPED UP, BUT SEKHON SWIFTLY MANOEUVRED HIS GNAT AND MANAGED TO STAY ON THEIR TAIL.

I'M TAILING THEM. I WON'T LET THEM...

...GET AWAY.

GOOD JOB, BROTHER! WHERE ARE YOU?

GHUMAN HAD LOST SIGHT OF THE SABRES AND HIS FELLOW GNAT BECAUSE OF THE THICK HAZE.

HE DECIDED TO DO AN OVERHEAD LAP, TO PROVIDE SUPPORT THE MOMENT HE COULD SPOT SEKHON.

BROTHER?

BUT THE RADIO HAD GONE SILENT.

*THE POINT IN AN OPTICAL INSTRUMENT WHICH CENTRES THE TARGET

SEKHON CONTINUED TO TRAIL CHANGAZI AND DOTANI AT TREETOP HEIGHT, AND BEGAN TO FIRE BULLETS.

HERE YOU ARE IN THE BULL'S EYE!

WE'RE BEING TAILED! DOTANI, JETTISON YOUR DROP TANKS* AND THROW HIM OFF.

DOTANI DROPPED HIS TANKS AND TOOK A HARD LEFT, NARROWLY AVOIDING SEKHON'S BULLETS.

THIS OUGHT TO SHAKE HIM OFF.

BUT THE NIMBLE GNAT TOOK AFTER HIM.

ANDRABI, ANOTHER PILOT ON THE PAKISTANI SQUAD, SPOTTED DOTANI BEING FIRED AT.

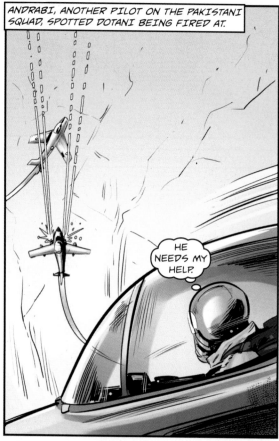

HE NEEDS MY HELP.

*DROP TANKS ARE RESERVE TANKS OF FUEL LOCATED EXTERNALLY ON AN AIRCRAFT'S BELLY. WHEN DROPPED, THEY SIGNIFICANTLY REDUCE THE WEIGHT ON THE AIRCRAFT, GIVING IT A BURST OF EXTRA SPEED.

ANDRABI FLEW TOWARDS SEKHON AND DOTANI.

DOTANI, BREAK! NOW!

DOTANI BROKE HARD, NARROWLY MISSING A COLLISION.

I'VE DODGED HIM FOR NOW. BUT MY SABRE IS CLOSE TO COLLAPSING.

RETREAT. HEAD BACK.

SO DOTANI FLEW WESTWARD INTO THE SHELTER OF THE MOUNTAINS.

THE PILOT OF THE FOURTH SABRE OF THE GROUP, MIR, HAD BEEN UNABLE TO LOCATE HIS FELLOW PILOTS.

DOTANI IS RETREATING, AND THE FOG'S MAKING ME BLIND.

SO MIR DECIDED TO FOLLOW DOTANI WESTWARDS.

A SABRE JUST DUCKED OUT. I'M FOLLOWING THE OTHER, BUT I'VE GOT ONE ON MY TAIL NOW.

NO WORD ...<CRACKLE>... FROM GHUMAN.

ANDRABI HAD STARTED FOLLOWING SEKHON, WHO WAS STILL CHASING CHANGAZI.

THE DOGFIGHT* CONTINUED, SEKHON SANDWICHED BETWEEN THE TWO.

AT LEAST I'VE MANAGED TO CHASE THEM OUT OF THE AIRFIELD. WE MUST BE ABOUT SIX KILOMETRES AWAY FROM THE AIRBASE.

EVEN THOUGH SEKHON AND THE SABRES WERE ONLY ABOUT 100 METRES ABOVE THE GROUND, THEY COULD NOT BE SEEN. FLYING OFFICER YOGINDRA SINGH (YOGI), WAS THE COMBAT AIR PATROL (C.A.P.) CONTROLLER AT THE BASE.

THERE'S DUST AND DEBRIS EVERYWHERE! ANY WORD ON GHUMAN, SIR?

NO, YOGI. THERE'S NO RESPONSE.

IT'S ALL UP TO SEKHON NOW.

*DOGFIGHT IS THE MILITARY TERM FOR CLOSE QUARTER COMBAT BETWEEN FIGHTER AIRCRAFT

I'M IN A CIRCLE OF JOY WITH TWO SABRES. I'M GETTING BEHIND ONE, BUT THE OTHER ONE IS GETTING AN EDGE ON ME.

SEKHON KEPT TRYING TO GET A HIT ON CHANGAZI WHILE TRYING TO AVOID BEING HIT BY ANDRABI BEHIND HIM.

BUT TRY AS HE DID, ANDRABI GOT NO HITS. AND SOON –

THREE IS WINCHESTER*.

HE HAD RUN OUT OF AMMUNITION.

CHANGAZI RADIOED BACK –

PLAY IT SAFE.

*MEMBERS OF A SQUAD IDENTIFY THEMSELVES BY NUMBERS. 'WINCHESTER' IS A MILITARY TERM USED WHEN ONE IS OUT OF AMMUNITION.

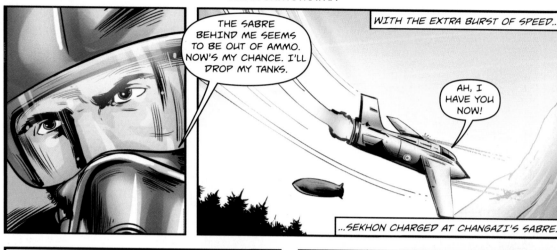

THE SABRE BEHIND ME SEEMS TO BE OUT OF AMMO. NOW'S MY CHANCE. I'LL DROP MY TANKS.

WITH THE EXTRA BURST OF SPEED...

AH, I HAVE YOU NOW!

...SEKHON CHARGED AT CHANGAZI'S SABRE.

BUT WHAT HE DID NOT KNOW WAS THAT PAKISTAN HAD AN ACE UP THEIR SLEEVE – TWO ACES, ACTUALLY.

BAIG AND YUSUFZAI WILL FLY WITH US AS ESCORTS TO PROVIDE SUPPORT. JUST IN CASE.

PAKISTAN HAD SET OUT WITH NOT FOUR, BUT SIX AIRCRAFT.

THESE TWO SABRES HAD BEEN CIRCLING THE AREA HIGH UP.

THE FIGHT'S GETTING FIERCER.

ANDRABI WILL GET HIM. HE'S AT HIS TAIL.

BUT WHEN ANDRABI FELL OUT...

CHANGAZI HAS NO SUPPORT. YUSUFZAI, IT'S TIME.

...THE TWO ESCORT AIRCRAFT SWOOPED DOWN.

WHAT...?

SEKHON DID NOT KNOW, AND HAD NOT SUSPECTED THE PRESENCE OF MORE SABRES.

BOTH AIRCRAFT BEGAN TO FIRE AT SEKHON SIMULTANEOUSLY.

GHUMAN... WHERE ARE YOU?

WHUMP!

I THINK I HAVE BEEN HIT. G MAN, COME AND GET THEM.

THE GNAT BEGAN TO LOSE HEIGHT.

THE SABRES CONTINUED TO RIDDLE THE GNAT WITH BULLETS.

SEKHON TRIED ONCE MORE TO CONTACT THE BASE, BUT –

THE FLIGHT CONTROL SYSTEM IS KNOCKED OUT. I AM LOSING ALTITUDE.

SEEING NO WAY OF RECOVERING HIS AIRCRAFT...

...SEKHON PULLED THE HANDLE ON HIS EJECTION SEAT.

THE GNAT CRASHED INTO A GORGE BELOW.

THE PAKISTANI SABRES RETURNED TO THEIR BASE.

SEKHON OPENED HIS PARACHUTE...

...BUT HE WAS TOO CLOSE TO THE GROUND.

IT DOESN'T HAVE ENOUGH TIME TO OPEN.

THE CANOPY OPENED BUT IT COULD NOT BE DEPLOYED PROPERLY.

AT THE BASE –

G MAN, YOU MADE IT BACK!

WHERE'S SEKHON?

THE OFFICERS AT THE BASE TOLD GHUMAN WHAT THEY HAD SEEN.

SEARCH PARTIES HAVE BEEN SENT OUT.

I SHOULD'VE BEEN THERE. I SHOULD'VE BEEN THERE.

IF IT WASN'T FOR HIM, WE WERE DONE FOR.

THE REMAINS OF THE GNAT WERE RECOVERED, BUT SEKHON WAS NEVER FOUND.

NIRMALJIT SINGH SEKHON WAS DECLARED DEAD, AND POSTHUMOUSLY AWARDED THE PARAM VIR CHAKRA FOR DEFENDING THE SRINAGAR AIRBASE, BRAVELY AND SINGLE-HANDEDLY.

FG OFFR NIRMALJIT SINGH SEKHON
1945 – 1971

HE IS THE ONLY AIR FORCE OFFICER TO HAVE WON THE PARAM VIR CHAKRA.

2/LT ARUN KHETARPAL

ARUN KHETARPAL WAS BORN INTO A FAMILY OF SOLDIERS. THE STRAPPING YOUNG BOY LOOKED EVERY INCH AN ARMY MAN.

WHICH UNIT ARE YOU FROM, SON?

HA HA! I AM STILL IN SCHOOL, SIR.

SO, WHEN HE JOINED THE N.D.A.* IN 1967, IT SEEMED LIKE THE PATH HE WAS MEANT TO TAKE.

IN 1970, HE MOVED TO THE INDIAN MILITARY ACADEMY AND PASSED OUT AS A COMMISSIONED OFFICER IN 1971.

HE WAS INDUCTED INTO 17 POONA HORSE, AN ARMOURED REGIMENT.

JUST SIX MONTHS LATER, IN OCTOBER, 1971 –

MA, MY REGIMENT HAS BEEN ASKED TO MOVE TO THE BORDER. I WILL BE LEAVING TOMORROW.

MY SON, YOUR GRANDFATHER, FATHER AND UNCLE HELD HIGH POSITIONS IN THE ARMY. DO NOT COME BACK LIKE A COWARD. FIGHT LIKE A TIGER.

THE CONFLICT BETWEEN WEST PAKISTAN AND EAST PAKISTAN WAS INCREASING. INDIA HAD DECIDED TO PROVIDE MILITARY SUPPORT TO EAST PAKISTAN.

*NATIONAL DEFENCE ACADEMY

AS A PREEMPTIVE MEASURE, THE INDIAN ARMY SENT MEN TO INDIA'S WESTERN BORDER.

I WANT OUR TANKS PLACED AT THESE LOCATIONS AND HIDDEN FROM SIGHT. THERE IS NO SIGN OF AN OFFENSIVE ATTACK RIGHT NOW, BUT WE HAVE TO BE FULLY PREPARED.

ON 3 DECEMBER –

ENEMY PLANES! TAKE COVER!

THE PLANES ARE LEAVING. OUR CAMOUFLAGE WAS PERFECT. THEY HAVEN'T HIT A SINGLE TANK!

THEY'VE LAUNCHED THEIR ATTACK. IT'S TIME FOR US TO MOVE FORWARD NOW.

BEFORE THE INDIAN ARMY COULD PROCEED, THEY HAD TO CLEAR THE AREA OF MINES.

THAT IS THE LAST MINE. WE ARE GOOD TO GO.

SIR, THE AREA HAS BEEN CLEARED. THE TANKS ARE READY TO PROCEED.

BY 10 DECEMBER, SQUADRON 'A' OF THE POONA HORSE REGIMENT HAD ADVANCED 16KM INTO ENEMY TERRITORY. ARUN WAS PART OF IT.

SQUADRON 'B' HAS MOVED UP TO JARPAL, IN THE SHAKARGARH SECTOR. IT'S ON THE OTHER SIDE OF BASANTAR RIVER.

YES. WE ARE TO STAY HERE IN CASE THEY NEED SUPPORT.

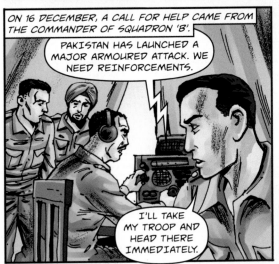

ON 16 DECEMBER, A CALL FOR HELP CAME FROM THE COMMANDER OF SQUADRON 'B'.

PAKISTAN HAS LAUNCHED A MAJOR ARMOURED ATTACK. WE NEED REINFORCEMENTS.

I'LL TAKE MY TROOP AND HEAD THERE IMMEDIATELY.

THE AREA IS FULL OF MINES. PROCEED WITH CAUTION.

YES, SIR.

JUST AS ARUN WAS ABOUT TO CROSS THE BASANTAR RIVER –

BOOM!

THE ATTACK IS COMING FROM THE R.C.L.* GUN NESTS ON THE SIDES.

*RECOILLESS GUNS

153

ARUN TURNED HIS TANK GUN AROUND AND SHOT DOWN ONE OF THE ENEMY GUN NESTS.

SIR, THEY HAVE A CLEAR VIEW OF THE FAMAGUSTA*!

IT DOESN'T MATTER. WE DON'T HAVE A MOMENT TO LOSE! MOVE THE TANK FORWARD.

WITH ARUN'S PRECISE INSTRUCTIONS, THE TANK MANOEUVRED THROUGH THE ONSLAUGHT AND SOON THEY WERE ACROSS THE RIVER.

AND THAT IS THE LAST ONE!

HEAD TO SQUADRON B'S POSITION.

ARUN HAD DESTROYED ALL THE ENEMY STRONGHOLDS!

*TANKS ARE GIVEN NAMES SO THAT IT IS EASY TO IDENTIFY ONE TANK FROM ANOTHER DURING BATTLE. FAMAGUSTA WAS THE NAME OF ARUN'S TANK.

JUST AS THEY ARRIVED AT THE POSITION –

THE PAKISTANI TANKS ARE RETREATING. QUICK! FOLLOW THEM.

CHARGED FROM THE BATTLE AT BASANTAR RIVER, ARUN WAS READY FOR ANOTHER FIGHT.

THAT TANK IS IN MY RANGE!

BOOM!

ARUN MANAGED TO DESTROY ONE OF THE RETREATING TANKS.

THOUGH DEFEATED, THE PAKISTAN SIDE DECIDED TO REGROUP AND LAUNCH A COUNTERATTACK.

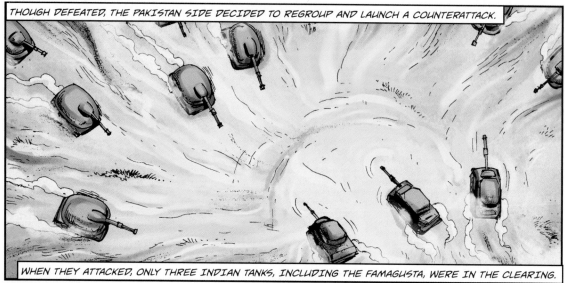

WHEN THEY ATTACKED, ONLY THREE INDIAN TANKS, INCLUDING THE FAMAGUSTA, WERE IN THE CLEARING.

BOOM!

SIR! YOU'VE BEEN HIT!

I AM OKAY. ATTACK THOSE TANKS!

PULL THE FAMAGUSTA BACK. <KZZT> THE TANK IS ON FIRE.

SIR, THE GUN IS STILL FUNCTIONING. I CAN STILL STOP THESE TANKS.

DESPITE BEING TOLD TO FALL BACK, ARUN PERSISTED. HE KNEW THAT FALLING BACK WOULD MEAN LOSING CONTROL OVER THE SECTOR.

THE OTHER TWO TANKS IN ARUN'S TROOP HAD BEEN DESTROYED. IT WAS UP TO ARUN TO FIGHT OFF THE REMAINING FOUR ENEMY TANKS.

FIRE!

MOVE TO THE RIGHT! FIRE!

THAT'S TWO TANKS DOWN AND TWO MORE TO GO!

BLAM!

BOOM!

ARUN HAD DESTROYED ANOTHER TANK.

IN THE OTHER TANK WAS THE COMMANDING OFFICER OF THE PAKISTANI SQUADRON, MAJOR NASER.

BOTH THE TANKS FIRED AT THE SAME TIME.

ARUN'S CANNON MISSED ITS MARK...

...BUT MAJOR NASER'S TANK HAD NOT.

21-YEAR-OLD 2/LT ARUN KHETARPAL WAS DEAD.

THE GALLANT COMMANDER OF THE FAMAGUSTA HAD NOT LET A SINGLE TANK PASS THROUGH.

HE HAD BEEN UNSTOPPABLE, TILL HIS LAST BREATH.

ARUN KHETARPAL WAS AWARDED THE PARAM VIR CHAKRA POSTHUMOUSLY.

HIS BRAVE ACT HAD GONE BEYOND THE CALL OF DUTY, FORCING THE ENEMY TO FALL BACK.

MAJOR HOSHIAR SINGH

ON THE ROHTAK–SONEPAT HIGHWAY IN HARYANA LIES SISNA, A FARMING VILLAGE THAT HAS BEEN HOME TO OVER 250 SOLDIERS OF THE INDIAN ARMY.

ON 5 MAY, 1937, WAS BORN THE MOST ILLUSTRIOUS OF THESE NAMES, HOSHIAR SINGH. HOSHIAR WAS A HARD-WORKING CHILD WHO GREW UP HELPING IN HIS FATHER'S FIELDS.

HOSHIAR, COME HAVE LUNCH!

ALMOST DONE, MA.

LIKE MANY IN HIS VILLAGE, HOSHIAR TOO ASPIRED TO JOIN THE ARMED FORCES FROM A YOUNG AGE. HE WAS RECRUITED WHEN HE WAS STILL A TEENAGER AT JAT COLLEGE IN ROHTAK.

DID YOU HEAR? HOSHIAR IS GOING TO BECOME A SOLDIER.

I'M NOT SURPRISED. THE ARMY IS ALL HE EVER TALKS ABOUT!

HOSHIAR WAS A NATURAL FIT AS A SOLDIER, BUT HE HAD BIGGER AMBITIONS.

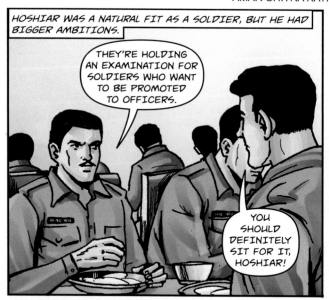

THEY'RE HOLDING AN EXAMINATION FOR SOLDIERS WHO WANT TO BE PROMOTED TO OFFICERS.

YOU SHOULD DEFINITELY SIT FOR IT, HOSHIAR!

HOSHIAR CLEARED THE EXAM IN HIS FIRST ATTEMPT. ON 30 JUNE, 1963 –

YOU WILL BE COMMISSIONED AS AN OFFICER IN THE GRENADIERS REGIMENT.

SIR!

HOSHIAR MOVED UP THE RANKS QUICKLY, EVENTUALLY BECOMING A MAJOR.

MAJOR SINGH IS ONE OF THE BEST LEADERS WE HAVE!

YES. HE'S HARD ON HIS MEN, BUT STILL RESPECTED BY EVERYONE.

YOU HAVE MORE STAMINA THAN ANYONE IN THE BATTALION, SIR. HOW DO YOU DO IT?

COMES FROM TILLING FIELDS FROM DAWN TO DUSK IN MY YOUTH!

THE DISCIPLINE AND THE STRICT ROUTINE THAT I HAD TO FOLLOW IN THOSE YEARS HELP ME EVEN NOW.

REMEMBER, MEN! BRAVERY ALONE ISN'T ENOUGH. YOU SHOULD ALSO KNOW WHAT TO DO WHEN BRAVERY IS REQUIRED! CONSTANT TRAINING AND PRACTICE IS A MUST FOR THIS!

HOSHIAR WAS ALSO ADMIRED FOR BEING A TEAM PLAYER. ONCE, AFTER RETURNING TO HIS UNIT FROM LEAVE —

SINGH, YOU'RE BACK! IT'S TOO BAD YOU COULDN'T COME IN TIME TO JOIN THE TEAM FOR THE BIG GAME.

WHAT GAME?

THE MEN ARE IN LADAKH FOR A VOLLEYBALL SERIES. THEY ARE MISSING YOU! THE TEAM IS A PLAYER SHORT AND THE FINAL IS TOMORROW.

TOMORROW? I CAN STILL MAKE IT!

HOSHIAR WAS A DIVISION VOLLEYBALL CHAMPION.

SIR, I NEED PERMISSION TO JOIN THE VOLLEYBALL TEAM IN LADAKH.

ABSOLUTELY NOT, SINGH! LADAKH IS A HIGH-ALTITUDE AREA. YOU'LL HAVE NO TIME TO ACCLIMATISE TO THE CONDITIONS.

THE TEAM HAS ALREADY BEEN THERE FOR OVER A WEEK. I CANNOT ALLOW YOU TO RISK YOUR HEALTH.

I HAVE TO GO, SIR! A WIN FOR THE BATTALION WILL MEAN A LOT.

HOSHIAR MANAGED TO CONVINCE HIS SENIOR OFFICER TO LET HIM GO. BUT WHEN HE ARRIVED IN LADAKH –

I CAN BARELY BREATHE.

EVERY SMALL EFFORT TOOK A LOT OF ENERGY. THE THIN AIR CAUSED HIM GREAT FATIGUE.

IGNORING THE CONDITIONS, HOSHIAR TOOK TO THE FIELD THE NEXT MORNING.

WE DIDN'T EXPECT YOU HERE, SIR!

JUST BEING HERE ISN'T ENOUGH, RAM SINGH. WE STILL HAVE A GAME TO WIN!

HOSHIAR IMPRESSED EVERYONE WITH HIS DETERMINATION. BUT HALFWAY THROUGH THE MATCH –

I CAN'T BREATHE.

GASP!

SIR!

HOSHIAR SINGH HAD TO BE EVACUATED IMMEDIATELY.

LATER –

SIR, WHY DID YOU PLAY WHEN YOU KNEW IT WAS SUCH A RISK?

I WAS JUST THINKING ABOUT MY TEAM.

THE YEAR 1971 BROUGHT THE TOUGHEST CHALLENGE MAJOR HOSHIAR SINGH AND HIS MEN WOULD EVER FACE. EAST PAKISTAN (BANGLADESH) DECLARED INDEPENDENCE FROM WEST PAKISTAN IN MARCH, 1971, AND THE TWO REGIONS HAD GONE TO WAR.

INDIA HAD GOT DRAWN INTO THE CONFLICT.

IN AN EFFORT TO DIVERT INDIAN TROOPS FROM HELPING EAST PAKISTAN IN THE EAST, THE WEST PAKISTANI FORCES HAD OPENED AN ATTACK ON THE WESTERN FRONT IN PUNJAB. THE COMMANDING OFFICER ADDRESSED HOSHIAR SINGH AND THE TROOPS.

WE HAVE RECEIVED INFORMATION THAT THE ENEMY IS ABOUT TO ATTACK THROUGH THE SHAKARGARH BULGE. AS YOU KNOW, THIS IS A KEY STRATEGIC AREA FOR US.

THE PAKISTANIS PLANNED TO CUT OFF NH1A WHICH WAS THE ONLY ROAD LINK BETWEEN JAMMU AND PUNJAB.

IF WE LOSE OUR GRASP HERE, JAMMU & KASHMIR WILL BE COMPLETELY CUT OFF FROM THE REST OF INDIA. RECAPTURING IT WILL COME AT A HUGE COST.

MAJOR SINGH! YOU WILL LEAD 'C' COMPANY TO THE VILLAGE OF JARPAL AND ESTABLISH A BRIDGEHEAD* ACROSS BASANTAR RIVER.

YES, SIR!

JARPAL OCCUPIED A KEY LOCATION IN SECURING CONTROL OVER THE SHAKARGARH BULGE.

YOUR TROOPS WILL HAVE TO PROCEED WITH GREAT CAUTION, SINGH! THE AREA IS FULL OF LANDMINES.

THE OBJECTIVE WILL BE ACHIEVED, SIR!

ON THE NIGHT OF 15 DECEMBER, 1971, HOSHIAR SINGH LED 'C' COMPANY TO JARPAL AND WAITED TO LAUNCH AN ATTACK.

REMEMBER YOUR TRAINING! STAY LOW AND PROCEED WITH CAUTION! THE PAKISTANIS HAVE ESTABLISHED DEFENSES EVERYWHERE.

AND WATCH OUT FOR LANDMINES! ONE WRONG STEP CAN MEAN DISASTER!

*AN AREA ACROSS AN OBSTACLE HELD BY THE ENEMY THROUGH WHICH LARGER OFFENSIVE FORCES, LIKE ARMOURED COLUMNS, ARE LAUNCHED TO EXPLOIT DEEP INTO ENEMY TERRITORY

DESPITE SUFFERING HEAVY CASUALTIES, MAJOR HOSHIAR SINGH'S 'C' COMPANY SCORED A HUGE VICTORY BY CAPTURING JARPAL FROM THE PAKISTANIS.

DON'T RELAX NOW, TROOPS. THE ENEMY IS SURE TO BE BACK!

HOSHIAR WAS RIGHT. THE NEXT DAY, ON 16 DECEMBER, THE PAKISTANI FORCES LAUNCHED THREE ATTACKS TO TRY AND RECAPTURE THE VILLAGE.

STAY STRONG, MEN! WE CANNOT GIVE THEM AN INCH!

BOOM!

TWO OF THE ATTACKS WERE SUPPORTED BY ARMOUR*.

WE CAN TAKE THEM! HOLD YOUR GROUND!

BOOM!

THE ENEMY ATTACKS WERE THWARTED AGAIN...

*HEAVILY ARMED TANKS THAT SUPPORT INFANTRY

...BUT THE PAKISTANI FORCES WERE NOT DONE. ON THE MORNING OF 17 DECEMBER, THEY LAUNCHED A FINAL ATTACK.

BOOM!

ARGH!

THE INDIAN TROOPS, LED BY HOSHIAR, FOUGHT WITH ALL THEY HAD.

SHABASH!* WE MUST BEAT THEIR ATTACK!

WITHOUT CARING ABOUT HIS SAFETY, HOSHIAR WENT FROM TRENCH TO TRENCH ENCOURAGING HIS MEN TO FIGHT BACK. THEN –

ZING

AAAAHH!

I MUST NOT GIVE UP!

JUST THEN –

BOOM!

AAAAHH!

*"VERY GOOD!"

170

INSPIRED BY HIS DETERMINATION, HOSHIAR'S MEN SHATTERED THE ENEMY ATTACK. THEIR COUNTER OFFENSIVE RESULTED IN 87 ENEMY SOLDIERS DEAD INCLUDING THE PAKISTANI COMMANDING OFFICER AND THREE OTHER OFFICERS.

SIR, WE MUST EVACUATE YOU!

NO, I MUST STAY TILL THE ENEMY IS DEFEATED!

THE BATTLE OF BASANTAR, AS IT WOULD COME TO BE CALLED, WAS ONE OF THE MOST CRUCIAL FIGHTS DURING THE INDO-PAK WAR OF 1971.

THEY'RE RETREATING!

WE'VE DONE IT!

AFTER THE WAR, MAJOR HOSHIAR SINGH WAS AWARDED THE PARAM VIR CHAKRA FOR HIS DISPLAY OF BRAVERY, DAUNTLESS COURAGE IN THE FACE OF HEAVY ODDS AND COMPLETE DISREGARD FOR HIS PERSONAL SAFETY.

HOSHIAR SINGH WAS PROMOTED TO THE RANK OF COLONEL BEFORE RETIRING FROM THE INDIAN ARMY.

NAIB SUBEDAR BANA SINGH

JUNE, 1987, SIACHEN: MORE THAN 21,153FT ABOVE SEA LEVEL.
THE 80-KILOMETRE-LONG SIACHEN GLACIER IS THE NORTHERNMOST TIP OF THE KARAKORAM RANGE OF THE HIMALAYAS. UNFORGIVINGLY COLD AND SURROUNDED ONLY BY SNOW, EVEN BREATHING AND MOVING ARE A STRUGGLE HERE.

CHUNNI, COME HERE! LOOK AT THIS TOOTHPASTE!

WHAT IS IT, BANA SA'AB?

IT'S FROZEN! HA HA!

HA HA HA!

WHEN THE TASK FORCE WAS FORMED, 38-YEAR-OLD BANA SINGH HAD BEEN THE FIRST TO VOLUNTEER.

WHO'S READY FOR THIS MISSION?

NAIB SUBEDAR BANA SINGH, SIR!

BANA SINGH AND CHUNNI LAL WERE BOTH PART OF A 62-MAN TASK FORCE – 57 JAWANS, TWO OFFICERS AND THREE J.C.O.S – WITHIN A BATTALION POSTED AT THE SIACHEN GLACIER. THEIR MISSION WAS TO TAKE BACK THE HIGHEST PEAK, NAMED QUAID POST.

QUAID POST HAD BEEN NAMED THUS AFTER PAKISTAN HAD CAPTURED IT IN 1984.

GOOD MORNING, SIR!

'MORNING.

SIR, IS THERE ANY NEWS ABOUT PHASE TWO?

PHASE ONE OF THE MISSION TO QUAID POST, THAT HAD BEEN SENT ON JUNE 23, HAD RETURNED UNSUCCESSFUL. TWO DAYS LATER, TEN JAWANS AND AN OFFICER HAD BEEN SENT AGAIN.

JUST THEN –

SIR, WE'VE LOST COMMUNICATION WITH THEM!

I WAS AFRAID OF THAT. NOTIFY THE C.O. IMMEDIATELY.

WE JUST RECEIVED WORD THAT THEY'VE MANAGED TO FIX THE ROPES.

THE MISSION WAS ABORTED, AND THE SECOND TEAM RETURNED THAT EVENING.

IN AN EARLIER MISSION TO CAPTURE THE POST, AN ARMY BATTALION HAD LAID DOWN ROPES TO ACCESS HIGHER ALTITUDES, BUT THE HEAVY SNOWFALL HAD COVERED THE ROPES AND THEY HAD TO BE FIXED AGAIN FOR THE OPERATION TO CONTINUE.

174

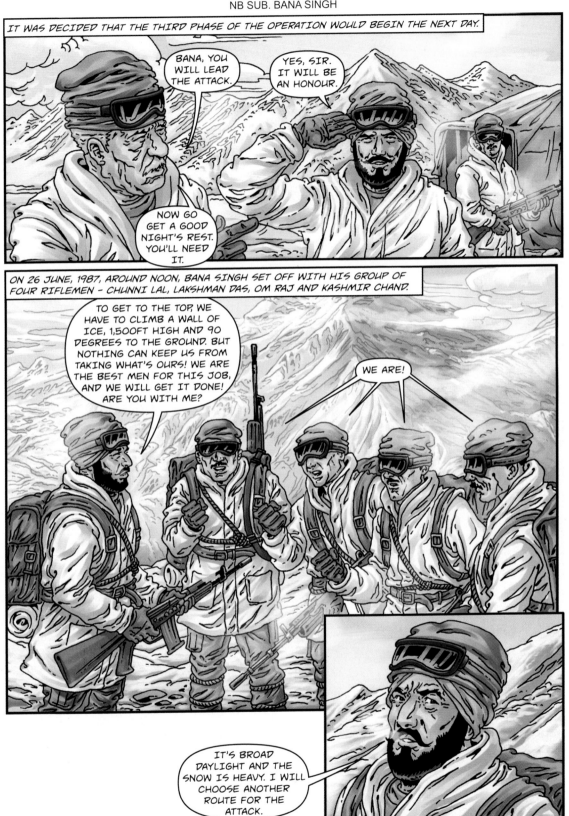

IT WAS DECIDED THAT THE THIRD PHASE OF THE OPERATION WOULD BEGIN THE NEXT DAY.

BANA, YOU WILL LEAD THE ATTACK.

YES, SIR. IT WILL BE AN HONOUR.

NOW GO GET A GOOD NIGHT'S REST. YOU'LL NEED IT.

ON 26 JUNE, 1987, AROUND NOON, BANA SINGH SET OFF WITH HIS GROUP OF FOUR RIFLEMEN – CHUNNI LAL, LAKSHMAN DAS, OM RAJ AND KASHMIR CHAND.

TO GET TO THE TOP, WE HAVE TO CLIMB A WALL OF ICE, 1,500FT HIGH AND 90 DEGREES TO THE GROUND. BUT NOTHING CAN KEEP US FROM TAKING WHAT'S OURS! WE ARE THE BEST MEN FOR THIS JOB, AND WE WILL GET IT DONE! ARE YOU WITH ME?

WE ARE!

IT'S BROAD DAYLIGHT AND THE SNOW IS HEAVY. I WILL CHOOSE ANOTHER ROUTE FOR THE ATTACK.

BANA SINGH FIXED THE ROUTE AND THE FIVE BEGAN THE CLIMB.

THE OXYGEN IS THIN UP HERE. WE SHOULD TAKE DEEP BREATHS.

DEEP BREATHS! EACH TIME I BREATHE, I'M ONE STEP CLOSER TO FROZEN ORGANS.

THEIR BATTALION HAD BEEN TRAINED IN MOUNTAIN WARFARE BY THE HIGH ALTITUDE WARFARE SCHOOL IN GULMARG AND SONAMARG.

....THERE'S NO SCOPE FOR HESITATION, BECAUSE YOU COULD LOSE A LIMB.

DON'T GIVE UP. MAKE SURE YOU HAVE A FIRM FOOTING BEFORE EACH STEP. SOFT SNOW CAN BE VERY TRICKY.

YOUR SURVIVAL DEPENDS ON THE STRENGTH OF THESE KNOTS.

SHIVERING AND EXHAUSTED, THE FIVE SOLDIERS FINISHED THEIR CLIMB.

WE'VE MADE IT TO THE TOP, SIR.

THERE'S THE POST. I THINK I SEE THEIR BUNKERS.

EVERY MINUTE THAT HE WAS LEADING THE MEN HIGHER, BANA REMEMBERED HIS TRAINING.

JUST THEN, THE INDIAN BATTALION STARTED GIVING THEM FIRE SUPPORT FROM BELOW. THE RETALIATION WAS SWIFT.

WHAT'S HAPPENING?

WHAT DO YOU THINK? THE PAKISTANIS ARE FIRING BACK.

TAKE COVER. NOW!

I DON'T HAVE A TARGET. THEY'RE SHOOTING FROM INSIDE THE BUNKER.

STAY DOWN, ALL OF YOU!

WHAT'S THE PLAN NOW? THEIR HIDEOUT LOOKS PRETTY STRONG.

YES IT DOES.

SO WHY ARE YOU SMILING, SA'AB?

BECAUSE A SAFE BUNKER EQUALS OVERCONFIDENCE. I HAVE A PLAN....

EVEN AS A CHILD, HE HAD BEEN FASCINATED WITH THE ARMY.

UNCLE, TELL ME STORIES OF THE ARMY!

OF COURSE, BANA!

ARMY LIFE IS VERY PRESTIGIOUS, SON. YOU SHOULD BE LIKE YOUR UNCLE WHEN YOU GROW UP.

HIS FATHER'S WORDS STUCK. IT WAS HIS 20TH BIRTHDAY WHEN HE ENROLLED IN 8 JAMMU & KASHMIR LIGHT INFANTRY (JAK LI).

I'M GIVING MYSELF THE MOST IMPORTANT BIRTHDAY PRESENT.

THE FIRING'S STOPPED COMPLETELY.

LOOK, THEY'RE COMING OUT OF THE BUNKER. JUST AS I THOUGHT.

PROBABLY TO INVESTIGATE THE SILENCE, THE PAKISTANI SOLDIERS HAD SLOWLY STARTED COMING OUT INTO THE OPEN.

ALL RIGHT, WE HAVE A CLEAR SHOT NOW. AT MY COMMAND, I WANT ALL OF YOU TO FIRE.

FIRE!

THE PAKISTANI SOLDIERS WERE TAKEN COMPLETELY BY SURPRISE.

AS THEY FIRED, THE FIVE SOLDIERS MOVED SWIFTLY THROUGH THE SNOW TOWARDS THE PAKISTANI BUNKER.

DON'T HOLD BACK! TRUST YOUR BAYONET!

BANA LOBBED A GRENADE IN THROUGH THE ENTRANCE OF THE BUNKER, WHILE THE OTHERS COVERED ALL THE EXITS.

WHAT FOLLOWED WAS A FIERCE CLOSE COMBAT FIGHT. THE PAKISTANI SOLDIERS WERE MORE IN NUMBER...

...BUT THE INDIANS WERE STRONGER AND WON THE DAY.

BANA SINGH RELAYED THE HAPPY MESSAGE.

WE'VE DONE IT, SIR! QUAID POST IS OURS.

THE ARMY LATER DECIDED TO RENAME THE POST BANA TOP IN HIS HONOUR.

ON 26 JANUARY, 1988, BANA SINGH WAS AWARDED INDIA'S HIGHEST MILITARY HONOUR. THE PRESIDENT OF INDIA, R. VENKATARAMAN, AWARDED HIM THE PARAM VIR CHAKRA.

....BANA SINGH DISPLAYED CONSPICUOUS GALLANTRY OF THE HIGHEST ORDER....

AT THE TIME, HE WAS THE ONLY PARAM VIR CHAKRA AWARDEE WHO WAS STILL SERVING IN THE ARMED FORCES. HE RETIRED AS A SUBEDAR MAJOR IN 2000, AND WAS ALSO MADE HONORARY CAPTAIN.

30 JULY, 1987,
DEHRADUN

MAJOR RAMASWAMY PARAMESWARAN WAS RELAXING AT HOME WITH HIS WIFE, UMA.

THIS IS WONDERFUL TEA, UMA! COULD YOU PASS ME THE PAPER, PLEASE?

THE PRIME MINISTER HAS SIGNED A PEACE ACCORD WITH SRI LANKA. WE'RE GOING TO SEND AN INDIAN PEACEKEEPING FORCE THERE.

YES, I DID SEE THE HEADLINES.

THE SITUATION IN SRI LANKA WAS TENSE. VELLUPILLAI PRABHAKARAN HAD FORMED A MILITANT ORGANISATION CALLED THE LIBERATION TIGERS OF TAMIL EELAM (L.T.T.E.) WITH THE AIM OF CREATING A SEPARATE STATE FOR TAMILS IN SRI LANKA.

THE L.T.T.E. AND THE SRI LANKAN GOVERNMENT WERE ENGAGED IN A CIVIL WAR.

SRI LANKAN PRESIDENT, JUNIUS RICHARD JAYEWARDENE, HAD REQUESTED INDIA'S PRIME MINISTER, RAJIV GANDHI, TO MEDIATE.

IT SOON BECAME CLEAR THAT THE L.T.T.E. HAD NO INTENTION OF HONOURING THE INDO-SRI LANKA ACCORD. THEY TURNED HOSTILE TOWARDS THE INDIAN TROOPS THAT HAD GONE THERE TO KEEP PEACE.

THE INDIAN GOVERNMENT DECIDED THAT IT WAS TIME FOR THE ARMY TO INTERVENE. TERMED OPERATION PAWAN, THE ARMY INITIALLY SENT A BRIGADE CONSISTING OF BATTALIONS FROM DIFFERENT REGIMENTS.

AMONG THESE, WAS 8 MAHAR REGIMENT.

MAJOR PARAMESWARAN, 'PARRY' TO HIS COLLEAGUES, WAS ITCHING TO BE PART OF THE ACTION.

I HAVE A REQUEST, SIR.

WHAT IS IT, PARRY?

I WISH TO JOIN 8 MAHAR, SIR.

PARRY'S REQUEST WAS GRANTED. ON 15 OCTOBER, 1987, HE LANDED AT THE PALAY AIRBASE IN SRI LANKA.

WELCOME TO JAFFNA, SIR.

THE PILOT TRIED TO LAND THE HELICOPTER BUT –

WE CAN BARELY SEE THE LANDING FIELD.

YOU'RE RIGHT. I AM TAKING HER UP.

LANDING IS NOT GOING TO BE EASY BUT I'LL GIVE IT ANOTHER TRY.

WITH GREAT PRECISION, THE PILOT BROUGHT THE HELICOPTER DOWN IN A SMALL CLEARING.

RUN FOR IT, MAJOR. GOOD LUCK!

THANK YOU!

MAJOR PARAMESWARAN MADE HIS WAY TO HIS LOCATION IN THE BATTALION.

BY NOVEMBER, THE L.T.T.E. HAD INCREASED ITS ATTACKS. MAJOR PARAMESWARAN WAS SHOWN THE CAMPS WHERE EVACUATED CIVILIANS WERE PUT UP.

IN THE MEANTIME, MAJOR PARAMESWARAN CONTINUED TO RECCE THE SURROUNDING AREA AND COLLECT INTELLIGENCE.

PARRY BEGAN TO VISIT THESE CAMPS FREQUENTLY. HE TRIED TO SEND THEM AS MANY SUPPLIES AS HE COULD.

MAJOR SA'AB, WE HAVE RUN OUT OF MEDICINE.

GIVE ME A LIST AND I'LL GET IT FOR YOU.

THE LOCALS, ESPECIALLY CHILDREN, LOVED THIS TAMIL-SPEAKING OFFICER WHO BROUGHT THEM SWEETS!

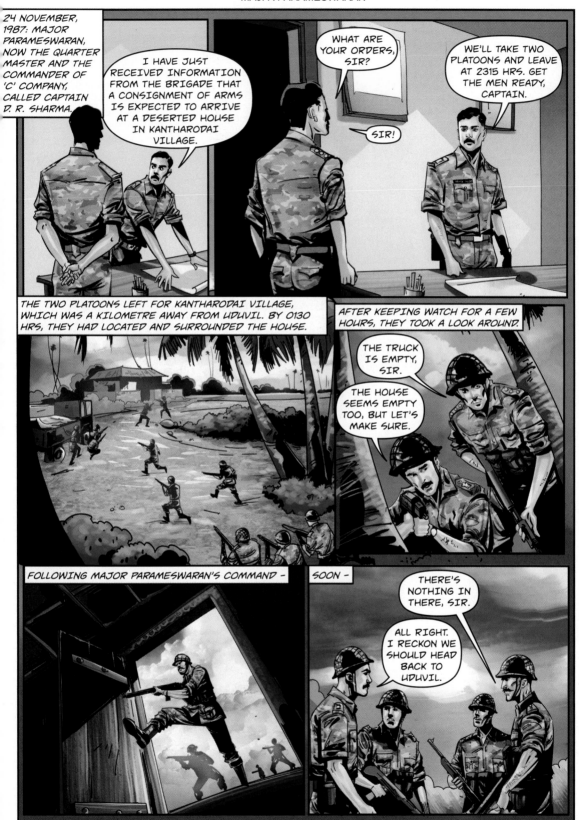

...BUT RETALIATED FIERCELY. THE SHEER NUMBER AND THE HEAVY FIRE THEY GENERATED BROKE THE INDIAN GROUP APART.

AS MAJOR PARAMESWARAN STEPPED INTO THE CLEARING –

AAH!

THE BULLET LEFT HIS PALM ALMOST SEVERED.

I'M FINE. CARRY ON!

HE SPRINTED TOWARDS THE NEAREST MILITANT, AND –

PARRY'S COURAGE GAVE THE MEN RENEWED FERVOUR.

FIRE!

SOON, THE MILITANTS SCATTERED AND BEGAN TO SEEK COVER.

WHEN CAPTAIN SHARMA REACHED MAJOR PARAMESWARAN AN HOUR LATER, HE HAD BREATHED HIS LAST.

EVEN HIS WATCH HAS STOPPED.

SOON AFTER, HELP ARRIVED IN THE FORM OF CAPTAIN T.C. BHATTACHARYA AND HIS TWENTY-MAN REINFORCEMENT.

THE BOLD MOVE PUT A SUDDEN END TO THE BATTLE. INFORMATION GATHERED FROM THE CAPTURED MILITANT ENABLED THEM TO RECOVER A HUGE AMOUNT OF EXPLOSIVES AND FIREARMS.

AN INTENSE BATTLE TOOK PLACE, DURING WHICH CAPTAIN BHATTACHARYA CHARGED INTO ONE OF THE TEMPLES AND CAPTURED A MILITANT.

FOR HIS INSPIRING LEADERSHIP AND EXTREME COURAGE, MAJOR RAMASWAMY PARAMESWARAN WAS HONOURED POSTHUMOUSLY WITH THE PARAM VIR CHAKRA.

UMA DONATED A LARGE SHARE OF THE BENEFITS SHE RECEIVED TO HELP CHILDREN AND WAR WIDOWS.

CAPTAIN MANOJ KUMAR PANDEY

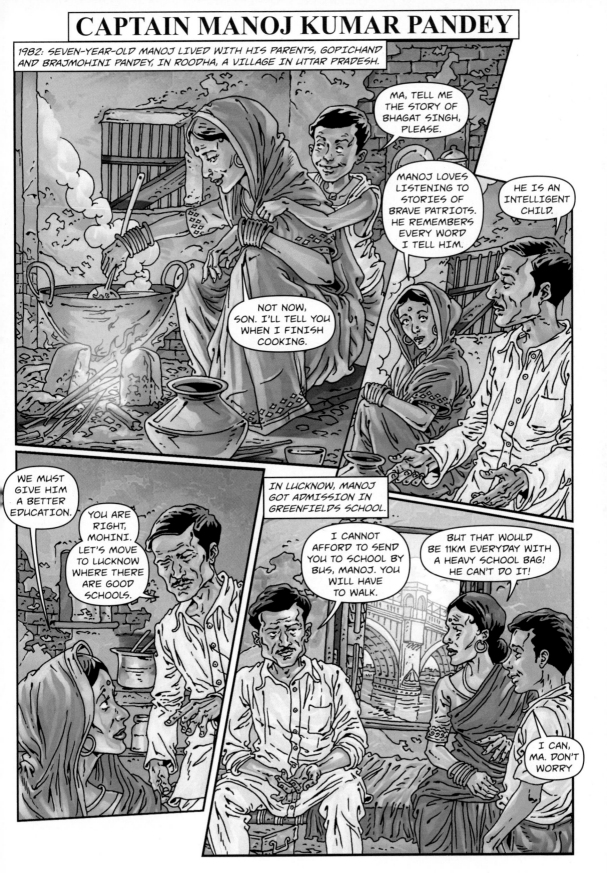

193

AS MANOJ GREW OLDER –

YOUR STUDIES ARE GETTING HARDER NOW. I WILL KEEP A TUTOR FOR YOU.

I DON'T NEED EXTRA COACHING, FATHER. I'LL STUDY ON MY OWN.

MANOJ DID WELL AT STUDIES. HE WAS ALSO KEEN ON BOXING AND BODYBUILDING.

YOUR FEET HARDLY TOUCH THE GROUND WHEN YOU SKIP. HOW DO YOU SKIP SO SILENTLY AND SO FAST?

I HAVE PLENTY OF PRACTICE AT HOME...

...AT NIGHT, MY MOTHER PUTS OUT THE CLAY POTS SHE MAKES TO DRY ON THE TERRACE. I PRACTISE SKIPPING OVER THE POTS AND BACK!

ONCE HE WAS GOING ON A SCHOOL TRIP TO HARIDWAR.

HERE. KEEP HUNDRED RUPEES WITH YOU FOR THE TRIP.

JUST GIVE ME THE CHANGE YOU HAVE.

MANOJ'S MOTHER GAVE HIM 24 RUPEES THAT SHE HAD WITH HER.

MANOJ RETURNED WITH RS 2. THE FAMILY SOON CAME TO KNOW WHAT HE HAD SPENT THE REMAINING MONEY ON.

THE POSTMAN HAS BROUGHT A MAGAZINE ADDRESSED TO YOU.

YES, MA. I BOUGHT A YEAR'S SUBSCRIPTION WITH THE MONEY YOU GAVE ME FOR THE TRIP. IT HAS STORIES ABOUT ALL OUR FREEDOM FIGHTERS.

MANOJ'S LOVE FOR HIS COUNTRY WAS EVIDENT EVEN AT THAT AGE.

AT N.D.A., MANOJ WAS SOON NOTICED BY SENIOR OFFICERS.

MARK MY WORDS. THAT YOUNG MANOJ PANDEY WILL GO A LONG WAY.

I FIND HIM A BIT RESERVED AND QUIET.

MAYBE. BUT HE HAS NERVES OF STEEL.

JUST THEN A SCUFFLE BROKE OUT BETWEEN TWO CADETS.

HOI! BREAK IT UP!

HE HAS SUCH A STENTORIAN VOICE!

HA! HA! YOU ARE RIGHT. GOOD VOICE FOR A LEADER!

MANOJ PASSED OUT FROM THE N.D.A. AND JOINED THE INDIAN MILITARY ACADEMY. IN JUNE, 1997, HE WAS COMMISSIONED AS AN OFFICER OF THE INDIAN ARMY.

I HAVE JOINED THE GORKHA RIFLES BATTALION. WE ARE POSTED IN KASHMIR.

AMMA, YOU TOLD ME STORIES OF BRAVEHEARTS LIKE BHAGAT SINGH AND AZAD. OF WHAT USE IS THAT AND ALL MY TRAINING IF I AM GOING TO BE SCARED OF CONFRONTING DANGER?

BUT HIS MOTHER COULD NOT GET OVER HER FEARS.

HE IS RIGHT.

MANOJ, I HAVE HEARD AN OFFICER IS ALWAYS BEHIND HIS TROOPS WHEN THEY ATTACK.

BUT THAT IS A HOTBED OF TERRORIST ACTIVITY!

AMMA, MY JAWANS ARE LIKE MY CHILDREN. I WILL ALWAYS LEAD FROM THE FRONT.

BUT IF YOU COME FACE-TO-FACE WITH THE ENEMY, CAN YOU KILL ANOTHER HUMAN BEING?

ON MANOJ'S FIRST ASSIGNMENT HIS SENIOR OFFICER WAS KILLED BY TERRORISTS IN AN AMBUSH.

AAAAH!

SIR!

ORDINARILY, NO. BUT IN WAR IF THERE IS A THREAT TO MY COUNTRY, I WILL. BECAUSE IF I DON'T KILL THEM THEY WILL KILL ME.

MANOJ WAS SO AFFECTED BY THE INCIDENT THAT HE WENT AFTER THE TERRORISTS...

MANOJ AND HIS WEARY UNIT HAD NO TIME TO REST.

SIR! POSTING ORDERS FOR 11 GORKHA.

...AND KILLED THREE DURING THAT VERY ASSIGNMENT.

WE ARE GOING TO SIACHEN. EVERYBODY REPORT TO THE OPERATIONS ROOM TOMORROW AT 0900 HRS.

SIACHEN GLACIER IS THE HIGHEST BATTLEGROUND IN THE WORLD.

IT IS SO BITTERLY COLD IN SIACHEN THAT YOU CAN SEE YOUR BREATH FREEZE UNDER YOUR NOSE! UNCOVERED FACES TURN BLACK WITH COLD.

DO NOT HANDLE YOUR FROZEN WEAPONS WITH BARE HANDS. WEAR GLOVES OR YOUR SKIN WILL STICK TO THE GUN AND GET RIPPED OFF.

THE UNIT HAD TO TRAIN IN MOUNTAIN-CLIMBING.

THE TERRAIN HERE IS TREACHEROUS. IT IS FULL OF CREVASSES. BEFORE CLIMBING WE FORM A ROPE CHAIN BY TYING OURSELVES TO ONE ANOTHER.

WHAT HAPPENS IF A PERSON FALLS OFF, SIR?

THE OFFICER'S REPLY WAS CHILLINGLY MATTER OF FACT.

WE ATTEMPT TO PULL UP THE PERSON QUICKLY. IF WE FAIL IN OUR ATTEMPT OF 4-5 MINUTES, WE CUT THE ROPE AND MOVE ON.

EQUIPPED WITH THIS NEW-FOUND KNOWLEDGE, THE UNIT WENT ON A CLIMB. AS THEY WERE GOING UP —

HEY! LOOK AT THAT!

MANOJ PANDEY WENT ON TO CREATE A PULLEY SYSTEM FOR CLIMBING, FOR WHICH HE WAS RECOMMENDED FOR THE SHAURYA CHAKRA.

*GROUND

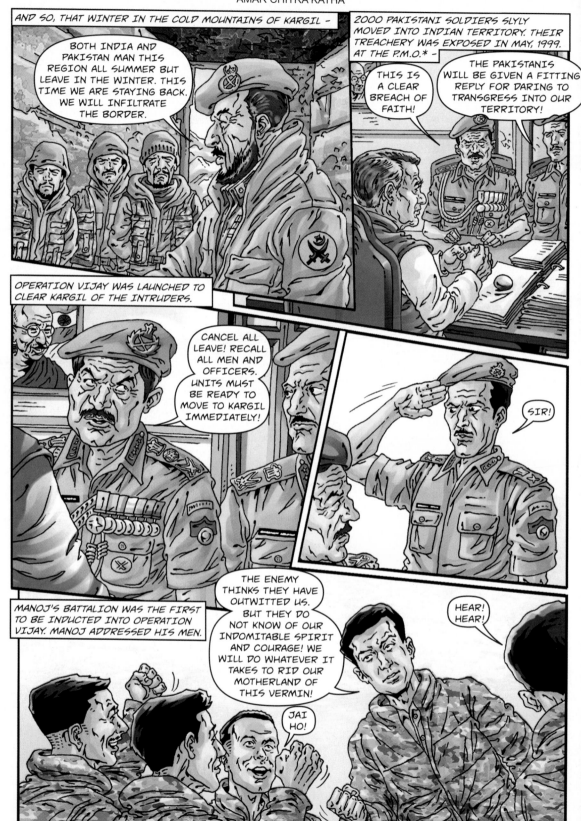

AND SO, THAT WINTER IN THE COLD MOUNTAINS OF KARGIL –

BOTH INDIA AND PAKISTAN MAN THIS REGION ALL SUMMER BUT LEAVE IN THE WINTER. THIS TIME WE ARE STAYING BACK. WE WILL INFILTRATE THE BORDER.

2000 PAKISTANI SOLDIERS SLYLY MOVED INTO INDIAN TERRITORY. THEIR TREACHERY WAS EXPOSED IN MAY, 1999. AT THE P.M.O.* –

THIS IS A CLEAR BREACH OF FAITH!

THE PAKISTANIS WILL BE GIVEN A FITTING REPLY FOR DARING TO TRANSGRESS INTO OUR TERRITORY!

OPERATION VIJAY WAS LAUNCHED TO CLEAR KARGIL OF THE INTRUDERS.

CANCEL ALL LEAVE! RECALL ALL MEN AND OFFICERS. UNITS MUST BE READY TO MOVE TO KARGIL IMMEDIATELY!

SIR!

MANOJ'S BATTALION WAS THE FIRST TO BE INDUCTED INTO OPERATION VIJAY. MANOJ ADDRESSED HIS MEN.

THE ENEMY THINKS THEY HAVE OUTWITTED US. BUT THEY DO NOT KNOW OF OUR INDOMITABLE SPIRIT AND COURAGE! WE WILL DO WHATEVER IT TAKES TO RID OUR MOTHERLAND OF THIS VERMIN!

HEAR! HEAR!

JAI HO!

*PRIME MINISTER'S OFFICE

MANOJ PANDEY MOVED WITH HIS UNIT TO BATALIK SECTOR, WHERE THERE WAS RELENTLESS FIRING.

THINGS ARE REALLY BLEAK HERE, PANDEY. WE HAVE MANY CASUALTIES FROM THE LAST AMBUSH.

BUT THE BODIES ARE IN ENEMY TERRITORY. YOU WILL GET THE BODIES BACK FROM THERE.

SIR!

THE OFFICER BRIEFING THEM WAS BRUTALLY FRANK.

THIS IS A VERY DANGEROUS MISSION. YOU HAVE NO MAPS TO GUIDE YOU. YOU WILL BE SITTING DUCKS AS THERE IS NO COVER IN THAT AREA.

THE OFFICERS WATCHED MANOJ AND THE UNIT CRAWL UP THE SLOPES INCH BY INCH.

BREATHING IS GOING TO BE VERY DIFFICULT AT THOSE ALTITUDES. EVEN MORE SO WITH THE HEAVY ARMS AND AMMUNITION THEY ARE CARRYING.

AND IT DID PROVE TO BE SO.

AAH!

QUICK! TAKE HIM DOWN!

201

AFTER THAT RISK-FRAUGHT MISSION, MANOJ PANDEY WAS PART OF A BOLDLY-LED ATTACK ON BATALIK HEIGHTS WHICH CLEARED THE JUBAR TOP OF INTRUDERS. IN A LETTER TO HIS PARENTS –

I assure you and my countrymen that whatever price we have to pay, we will chase away the intruders. Many of our soldiers have attained martyrdom but I am still alive, maybe to attain some higher aim

SOON AFTER, MANOJ BECAME COMMANDER OF NO.5 PLATOON. ON THE NIGHT OF 2 JULY, 1999 –

OLTHINGTHANG
5287 KUKARTHANG
4927
JUBAR A812
KHALUBAR
CHULICHANG
BATALIK
DAH

THIS IS THE BUNKER AREA OF KHALUBAR HEIGHTS IN THE BATALIK SECTOR. THE ENEMY IS COMFORTABLE THERE IN BUNKERS AND ANY ATTEMPT BY OUR TROOPS TO ADVANCE TO THE TOP IS MET WITH GUNFIRE...

...IT IS A 7-HOUR CLIMB TO THE TOP IN TOUGH AND UNFORGIVING TERRAIN. WORSE STILL, THE ENEMY IS ARMED WITH HIGHLY SOPHISTICATED WEAPONS.

SIR! WE ARE NOT AFRAID OF THE TERRAIN OR THE WEATHER OR OF THE ENEMY AND HIS WEAPONS. JUST GIVE US ENOUGH AMMUNITION AND THE ORDERS TO MOVE!

HEAR! HEAR!

ORDERS TAKEN, MANOJ AND HIS MEN MOVED STEALTHILY ALONG A NARROW RIDGE WHICH LED TO THE SLOPES THEY WERE TO CLIMB.

MANOJ LED HIS MEN UP THE 80 DEGREE SLOPE. THE PLATOON INCHED UP BUFFETED BY ICY WINDS AND A CONTINUOUS BARRAGE OF ENEMY GUNFIRE. THEIR ONLY THOUGHT – CLEAR THE BUNKERS OF THE ENEMY.

WHEN THEY REACHED THE TOP, MANOJ PANDEY OUTLINED HIS STRATEGY.

YOU WILL CLEAR THE BUNKERS ON THE RIGHT. I AM GOING TO DESTROY THE FOUR BUNKERS ON THE LEFT.

AT THE CRACK OF DAWN, MANOJ AND HIS PLATOON LAUNCHED A DARING ATTACK.

HIS MEN SAW HIM FALL AND CAME RUNNING. BUT HE SHOUTED TO THEM –

NA CHHORNU! NA CHHORNU!*

WE HAVE DRIVEN THEM AWAY, SIR!

MAD WITH GRIEF AND ANGER AT SEEING THEIR BELOVED COMRADE DYING, CAPTAIN PANDEY'S MEN WENT ON A RAMPAGE AND DECIMATED THE ENEMY.

THE TEAM CAME BACK TO REPORT THAT MANY HAD BEEN KILLED IN THE ENEMY RANKS. SOME HAD RUN AWAY, LEAVING BEHIND A HUGE CACHE OF ARMS AND AMMUNITION. FROM THE INDIAN SIDE, SIX SOLDIERS HAD LOST THEIR LIVES ALONG WITH MANOJ PANDEY.

CAPTAIN MANOJ PANDEY RETURNED HOME A HERO. HIS BODY WAS FLOWN BACK TO LUCKNOW. MANY PEOPLE LINED THE FLOWER-BEDECKED ROUTE FROM HIS HOME TO THE FINAL RESTING PLACE.

*IN GORKHALI – "DON'T LEAVE THEM!"

205

24-YEAR-OLD MANOJ PANDEY RECEIVED THE NATION'S HIGHEST ORDER OF GALLANTRY - THE PARAM VIR CHAKRA. IT WAS THE FIRST PARAM VIR CHAKRA OF THE KARGIL WAR.

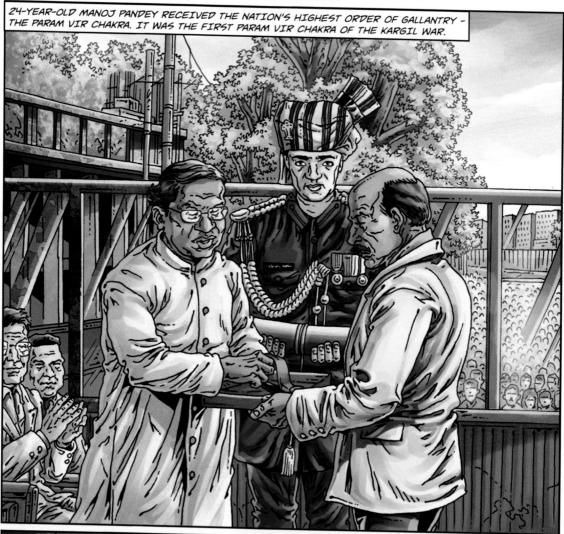

CAPTAIN MANOJ PANDEY WROTE REGULARLY IN HIS DIARY. AN EXCERPT FROM HIS DIARY -

If death should strike before I prove my blood, I swear I will kill death.

GRENADIER YOGENDRA SINGH YADAV

THE YEAR WAS 1996. 16-YEAR-OLD YOGENDRA SINGH YADAV HAD JUST JOINED THE 18 GRENADIERS REGIMENT OF THE INDIAN ARMY.

YADAV, YOU WILL JOIN THE GHATAK PLATOON FOR TRAINING IMMEDIATELY.

YES, SIR!

ONLY THE MOST PHYSICALLY FIT AND MOTIVATED SOLDIERS WERE SELECTED TO BE A PART OF THE GHATAKS.

YOU WILL NEED TO BUILD YOUR STAMINA TO CARRY FOOD AND AMMUNITION OVER LONG DISTANCES.

GHATAK COMMANDOS WERE TRAINED IN SURVIVAL TACTICS TO ENDURE THE MOST ADVERSE CONDITIONS.

GRENADIER YOGENDRA CAME THROUGH THE TRAINING WITH AN OUTSTANDING REPORT, EXCELLING IN ALL THE TASKS ASSIGNED TO HIM.

PUT THE RIFLE TOGETHER IN 45 SECONDS!

CHAK!

WELL DONE, YADAV! YOU'VE FINISHED WITH TIME TO SPARE.

THREE YEARS LATER, IN 1999, YOGENDRA GOT MARRIED. HOWEVER, HIS JOY PROVED TO BE SHORT-LIVED, AS JUST A FEW DAYS AFTER THE WEDDING –

THIS ISN'T RIGHT!

WHAT HAPPENED?

PAKISTANI MILITANTS HAVE OCCUPIED INDIAN BUNKERS IN KASHMIR.

INDIA AND PAKISTAN HAD A PACT WHICH STATED THAT BOTH SIDES WOULD VACATE THE AREA DURING WINTERS TO AVOID THE HARSH WEATHER. THE ARMY POSTS HAD BEEN EMPTY AS A RESULT.

I MUST RETURN TO MY UNIT IN SRINAGAR IMMEDIATELY!

BUT YOUR LEAVE ISN'T OVER.

I MIGHT BE NEEDED, REEMA. HOW CAN I JUST STAY HERE WHEN OUR COUNTRY IS UNDER ATTACK?

YOU'RE RIGHT. I KNOW YOU HAVE TO GO. BUT PLEASE STAY SAFE.

YOGENDRA VOLUNTARILY CUT SHORT HIS LEAVE AND REJOINED HIS UNIT. SOON AFTER, THERE WAS SOME DISTURBING NEWS.

THEY'RE SAYING THAT SOLDIERS FROM THE PAKISTANI ARMY ARE ALSO INVOLVED IN THE INTRUSION.

WHAT?! HOW CAN THEY JUST VIOLATE THE TRUCE LIKE THAT? THIS WOULD MEAN US GOING TO WAR.

YOGENDRA WAS RIGHT. ONCE THE PAKISTANI ARMY'S INVOLVEMENT WAS CONFIRMED IN MAY 1999, A FULL-SCALE WAR BROKE OUT BETWEEN THE TWO COUNTRIES.

A FEW WEEKS INTO THE FIGHTING, INDIA HAD SUCCESSFULLY CLEARED MOST OF THE POSTS OCCUPIED BY THE ENEMY FORCES. ONE BASE THAT WAS YET TO BE CAPTURED WAS TIGER HILL TOP IN KARGIL.

WE HAVE ALREADY RECLAIMED THE NORTH, SOUTH AND EAST FACES OF TIGER HILL. THE GHATAK PLATOON HAS BEEN CHOSEN TO LEAD THE ATTACK ON THE WESTERN FACE.

IT WAS A 16,500-FOOT VERTICAL CLIMB TO THE TOP.

WE WILL SCALE THE MOUNTAIN AT NIGHT AND SET UP AN M.M.G. BASE AT 16,000FT, BEFORE PROCEEDING HIGHER.

YOGENDRA WENT TO LIEUTENANT BALWAN AFTER THE BRIEFING.

YES, YADAV?

I WOULD LIKE TO LEAD THE CLIMB, SIR!

IT'S A DANGEROUS ASCENT AND THE ICY SURFACE WILL BE HIGHLY SLIPPERY AND UNRELIABLE.

IT'S WHAT WE'VE BEEN TRAINED FOR, SIR!

VERY WELL. DON'T LET US DOWN, YADAV! BE CAREFUL.

AND SO, UNMINDFUL OF THE RISK, YOGENDRA LED THE GHATAKS UP TIGER HILL BY CLIMBING FIRST AND TYING THE ANCHORING ROPES FOR THE REST OF THE TROOPS TO FOLLOW.

SLOWLY, BUT STEADILY, THE PLATOON MADE ITS WAY TO THE FIRST TARGET OF 16,000FT THROUGH THE BITING COLD.

DAWN IS BREAKING. WE WILL SET UP BASE HERE AND CLIMB THE REMAINING 500FT AFTER SUNDOWN.

THAT NIGHT, ON JULY 3, 1999, THE GHATAKS LAUNCHED A FINAL SURGE TOWARDS THE SUMMIT IN COMPLETE DARKNESS.

BUT KEEPING A WATCH ON THE CONDITIONS AND THE ENEMY WAS NOT EASY AND THE PLATOON WAS SPOTTED BEFORE IT COULD REACH THE BUNKERS.

THERE ARE THREE ENEMY BUNKERS GUARDING THIS APPROACH. BE VERY QUIET!

ENEMY APPROACHING! FIRE!

TAKE COVER! TAKE COVER!

ONLY SEVEN INDIAN COMMANDOS, INCLUDING YOGENDRA, MANAGED TO SCRAPE THROUGH THE FIRING. THE REST OF THE TROOPS REMAINED AT THE M.M.G. BASE BELOW.

WE MUST KEEP MOVING FORWARD!

AND THEN –

I'M HIT.

YOGENDRA HAD SUSTAINED THREE BULLET WOUNDS IN HIS LEFT HAND DURING THE EXCHANGE OF FIRE. HOWEVER –

WE'RE ONLY 60 METRES FROM THE TOP! I MUST MAKE IT!

ONCE THE FIRST ENEMY BUNKER WAS IN SIGHT, YOGENDRA KNEW HE COULD BOMB THEM.

THE GRENADE FOUND ITS MARK.

BUOYED BY THE CAPTURE OF THE FIRST POST, THE REMAINING GHATAKS PLOUGHED FORWARD, WITH YOGENDRA LAGGING A BIT BECAUSE OF HIS WOUNDS.

THERE'S ANOTHER BUNKER WHERE THOSE SHOTS ARE COMING FROM. MAKE YOUR WAY THERE!

AS YOGENDRA TRIED TO CATCH UP, HE NOTICED SOMETHING STARTLING AHEAD.

OUR MEN ARE BEING FOLLOWED!

WITHOUT WASTING A MOMENT, HE LOBBED A GRENADE AT THE PAKISTANI SOLDIERS STALKING HIS MATES.

BOOM!

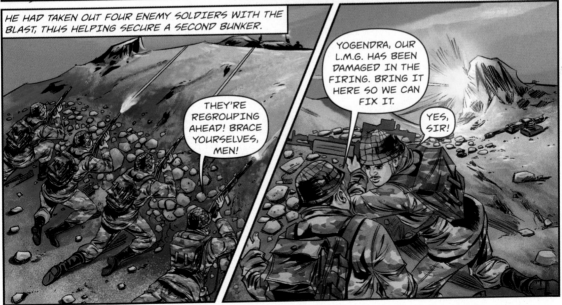

HE HAD TAKEN OUT FOUR ENEMY SOLDIERS WITH THE BLAST, THUS HELPING SECURE A SECOND BUNKER.

THEY'RE REGROUPING AHEAD! BRACE YOURSELVES, MEN!

YOGENDRA, OUR L.M.G. HAS BEEN DAMAGED IN THE FIRING. BRING IT HERE SO WE CAN FIX IT.

YES, SIR!

DESPITE BEING WOUNDED AND HAVING NO COVER, YOGENDRA RAN TOWARDS THE L.M.G. WITHOUT HESITATION. JUST THEN –

BOOM!

AAAH!

THE BLAST CAUGHT YOGENDRA BUT DID NOT DETER HIM.

YOGENDRA, YOU'RE BADLY WOUNDED. YOU MUST BE EVACUATED!

NO! WE HAVE TO ACHIEVE THE OBJECTIVE FIRST!

REALISING THAT THEY WERE GETTING CORNERED, YOGENDRA RUSHED TO TAKE COVER IN A NEW POSITION. BUT –

AAAH!

THE SPLINTERS FROM THE GRENADE TORE INTO HIS LEGS. A SECOND BLAST SENT MORE TOWARDS HIS NOSE AND FACE.

I... MUST... NOT... RETREAT!

THE MAIN ENEMY BUNKER WAS JUST 50 METRES AWAY, BUT ONLY FIVE INDIAN COMMANDOS REMAINED STANDING.

THEY'RE WALKING TOWARDS US!

THEY MUST HAVE REALISED THAT WE'RE OUTNUMBERED.

THE PAKISTANI SOLDIERS KEPT FIRING TILL THEY REACHED THE INDIANS.

I THINK WE GOT THEM ALL. CALL COMMANDER SAHIB.

INDEED, ALL THE INDIANS HAD BEEN FATALLY HIT – ALL, EXCEPT ONE!

I'M STILL ALIVE! BUT I CAN'T LET THEM KNOW THAT.

THE CLOCK HAD TICKED PAST MIDNIGHT TO 4 JULY BY NOW. YOGENDRA LAY THERE, PRETENDING TO BE DEAD, TILL THE COMMANDER OF THE ENEMY TROOPS ARRIVED AN HOUR LATER.

TAKE AWAY THEIR RIFLES AND MAKE SURE THERE ARE NO SURVIVORS! PREPARE TO ATTACK THEIR M.M.G. BASE RIGHT AFTER!

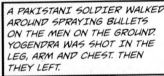

A PAKISTANI SOLDIER WALKED AROUND SPRAYING BULLETS ON THE MEN ON THE GROUND. YOGENDRA WAS SHOT IN THE LEG, ARM AND CHEST. THEN THEY LEFT.

I AM STILL ALIVE!

BUT HOW?

THE COINS IN MY WALLET MUST HAVE DEFLECTED THE BULLET TO MY CHEST!

AS YOGENDRA LOOKED AROUND —

NONE OF THEM HAVE BEEN SPARED BY THE PAKISTANIS. I MUST AVENGE THEIR DEATHS!

I MUST REACH OUR M.M.G. BASE BELOW AND WARN THEM!

BUT —

OH NO! THE PAKISTANIS ARE ALREADY AHEAD OF ME. I HAVE TO TAKE THEM OUT!

YOGENDRA STILL HAD TWO GRENADES LEFT WITH HIM.

THE GRENADES KILLED ONE OF THE ENEMY SOLDIERS.

BRUISED, BATTERED AND INJURED WITH MULTIPLE BULLET WOUNDS, YOGENDRA WAS HELPED TO THE BUNKER BY HIS FELLOW SOLDIERS.

THE PAKISTANIS ARE HEADED HERE. YOU MUST BE PREPARED!

WARNED IN TIME, THE INDIAN TROOPS SUCCESSFULLY REPELLED THE ENEMY...

...AND THE THREE-BUNKER TIGER HILL TOP WAS RECAPTURED BY THE INDIANS.

YOGENDRA SINGH YADAV WAS AWARDED THE PARAM VIR CHAKRA FOR HIS SUSTAINED DISPLAY OF BRAVERY, AT THE AGE OF 19.

HE HAS BEEN SINCE PROMOTED TO THE RANK OF SUBEDAR.

RIFLEMAN SANJAY KUMAR

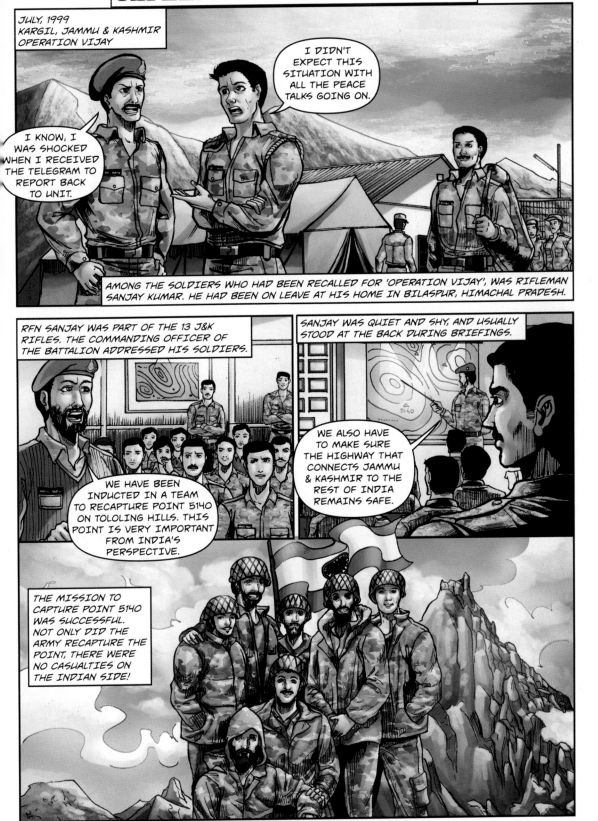

SOON AFTER THE CAPTURE OF POINT 5140, THE MEN OF 13 J&K RIFLES WERE TOLD TO TAKE CONTROL OF POINT 4875. TWO PARTIES WERE TO LEAD AND THE REST WERE TO BRING UP THE REAR. DURING THE BRIEFING –

ANY QUESTIONS?

I WANT TO BE IN THE LEADING PARTY, SIR.

ON 4 JULY, 1999, THE LEADING PARTY WAS TASKED WITH CAPTURING A FLAT, ROCKY PART OF THE MOUNTAIN WHICH WOULD MAKE RECAPTURING POINT 4875 EASIER.

I MUST FIGHT FOR THE SAFETY OF MY LOVED ONES, FOR ALL THOSE I HAVE LEFT BEHIND IN BILASPUR.

AS THE TROOPS CLIMBED, SANJAY'S THOUGHTS DRIFTED TO THE DAY HE HAD TO LEAVE FOR THE WAR.

IT IS GREAT TO HAVE YOU BACK. WE ARE FINALLY GETTING MARRIED!

I KNOW. IT IS A WONDERFUL FEELING.

AS THE TROOPS CLIMBED, THE TERRAIN GOT BARER AND TOUGHER.

THE TASK WAS MADE EVEN MORE DANGEROUS BY THE FACT THAT IT WAS A DAYLIGHT MISSION.

AS THEY NEARED POINT 4875 —

TRA GA DA GA

TRA GA DA GA

TAKE COVER!

THE ADVANCING TROOPS SUDDENLY FOUND THEMSELVES CAUGHT IN HEAVY FIRING.

SIR, THE ENEMY CAN SPOT US EASILY.

WE WILL HAVE TO PROCEED WITH CAUTION. USE EVERY POSSIBLE COVER THERE IS.

THE LEADING PARTY INCHED THEIR WAY UP, WHILE THE SOLDIERS IN THE REAR GAVE THEM COVER. BUT —

STOP COVER FIRE. WE ARE RIGHT IN THE WAY. YOU WILL HARM US MORE THAN THE PAKISTANIS!

YES, SIR! WE WILL HOLD BACK FIRE.

WITHOUT ANY COVER FIRE, THE TEAM HAD TO RELY ON LUCK AND THE FEW ROCKS THAT SEPARATED THEM FROM THE PAKISTANI MACHINE GUNS.

BLEEDING PROFUSELY FROM HIS WOUNDS...

...SANJAY CREPT UP TO THE BUNKER...

...FROM WHERE THE PAKISTANIS WERE FIRING THEIR UNIVERSAL MACHINE GUN, INCESSANTLY.

DURGA MATA KI JAI*!

SURPRISED BY SANJAY'S APPEARANCE, THE PAKISTANIS RAN LEAVING BEHIND THEIR MACHINE GUN.

SANJAY CAUGHT THE BURNING HOT BARREL OF THE GUN WITH HIS BARE HANDS...

...AND TURNING IT AROUND, FIRED AT THE ENEMY.

TRA-GA-DA-GA

*BATTLE CRY OF JAMMU & KASHMIR RIFLES

RIFLEMAN SANJAY'S ACT CHARGED UP HIS COMRADES.

DURGA MATA KI JAI!

MEANWHILE –

YOU ARE BADLY INJURED, WE NEED TO GET YOU OUT OF HERE.

NO! GO AHEAD. CAPTURING THE POINT IS MORE IMPORTANT. I WILL BE FINE.

THE INDIAN ARMY POURED FORWARD, THWARTING ANY ENEMY FORCE THAT CAME THEIR WAY.

THE ENEMY WAS BEATEN, AND THE FLAT TOP, CAPTURED.

EVEN THOUGH SANJAY WAS BADLY INJURED AND LOSING BLOOD, HE REFUSED TO BE EVACUATED.

POINT 4875 HAD BEEN OCCUPIED. SANJAY'S ACT HAD MADE IT EASIER FOR THE INDIAN TROOPS TO MOVE FORWARD.

WHEN THE RESCUE AND MEDICAL TEAM ARRIVED AT THE SPOT –

THERE ARE VERY FEW SURVIVORS.

WE NEED TO EVACUATE ALL THE INJURED SOLDIERS FIRST.

SIR! THIS MAN IS STILL BREATHING.

THE SOLDIER WAS SANJAY! HE HAD LOST A LOT OF BLOOD AND WAS CRITICALLY INJURED, BUT HE WAS ALIVE!

GET HIM TO THE BASE IMMEDIATELY.

A MEDICAL TEAM WORKED TIRELESSLY ON SANJAY AND SAVED HIS LIFE.

THIS MAN WILL LIVE TO TELL HIS TALE.

WHEN HE WENT HOME...

SANJAY ZINDABAD!

...HIS VILLAGE GAVE HIM A HERO'S WELCOME!

SANJAY KUMAR WAS AWARDED THE PARAM VIR CHAKRA FOR HIS EXEMPLARY COURAGE IN BATTLE. WHEN ASKED TO COMMENT, THE HERO HAD ONLY ONE THING TO SAY –

I HAVEN'T DONE ANYTHING DIFFERENT. ANYONE IN MY PLACE WOULD HAD DONE THE SAME THING.

CAPTAIN VIKRAM BATRA

GIRDHARI LAL BATRA WAS TELLING HIS CHILDREN THE STORY OF INDIA'S FREEDOM STRUGGLE.

....AND THAT IS HOW THE BRAVE BHAGAT SINGH GAVE UP HIS LIFE FOR INDIA'S FREEDOM.

EVERY NIGHT, AT THEIR HOME IN PALAMPUR, HE WOULD SIT DOWN WITH HIS TWO DAUGHTERS AND THE TWINS, VIKRAM AND VISHAL, AND TELL THEM INSPIRING STORIES.

THE CHILDREN, PARTICULARLY VIKRAM, GREW UP WITH A STRONG SENSE OF PRIDE IN THEIR COUNTRY. WHEN VIKRAM GOT ACCEPTED IN THE MERCHANT NAVY –

I KNOW I WILL EARN A LOT MORE IN THE MERCHANT NAVY, BUT I WANT TO JOIN THE ARMY.

BUT....

THIS IS WHAT I WANT TO DO, PAPA.

THE FAMILY AGREED OF COURSE AND IN 1997, VIKRAM BATRA PASSED OUT OF THE INDIAN MILITARY ACADEMY AS AN ARMY OFFICER.

HE WAS INDUCTED INTO THE 13 J&K RIFLES.

ON 1 JUNE, 1999, VIKRAM'S UNIT WAS MOVED TO KARGIL. THERE WAS TROUBLE BREWING IN JAMMU & KASHMIR.

OUR PATROL PARTY HAS BEEN AMBUSHED AND KILLED! THEY HAVE NOT SPARED A SINGLE SOLDIER.

PAKISTAN HAD MOVED INTO INDIAN TERRITORY AND OCCUPIED MUSHKOH VALLEY AND THE DRAS AND BATALIK SECTORS.

ON 12 JUNE, 1999, VIKRAM'S BATTALION WAS SHIFTED TO DRAS. THEY WERE TASKED WITH RECAPTURING A HILL CALLED THE 'HUMP'. IT WAS AN EXTENSION OF THE TOLOLING RIDGE.

AT 15,500FT THIS WAS NOT AN EASY TASK. BRAVING SUB-ZERO TEMPERATURE, THE BATTALION MOVED AHEAD.

SOON –

SIR, THE 'HUMP' HAS BEEN CAPTURED!

TWO COMPANIES WERE TASKED WITH THE CAPTURE OF THIS POINT. BRAVO COMPANY, COMMANDED BY CAPTAIN JAMWAL, AND DELTA COMPANY BY CAPTAIN VIKRAM BATRA.

*DURING WARTIME, SOLDIERS WERE GIVEN CODE NAMES. SHERSHAH, MEANING 'LION KING', WAS VIKRAM BATRA'S CODE NAME.

231

VIKRAM AND JAMWAL TOOK THEIR POSITIONS WITH THEIR MEN AT THE 'HUMP'.

WHAT IS THE PLAN, SIR?

WE MOVE UP ONCE THE LIGHT BEGINS TO FADE. WE HAVE TO CLEAR THE AREA BEFORE DAYLIGHT.

WE WILL CLIMB FROM THE REAR. THE PAKISTANI TROOPS WILL EXPECT US TO COME FROM THE FRONT.

THEY WILL NEVER DREAM THAT WE WOULD ATTEMPT THE CLIMB FROM THE BACK.

THE CLIMB VIKRAM HAD SUGGESTED WAS ALMOST VERTICAL, AND VERY DANGEROUS.

LED BY VIKRAM, DELTA COMPANY BEGAN ITS CLIMB.

DON'T LOOK DOWN. JUST KEEP GOING. WE CAN DO THIS!

THE RARIFIED* AIR AT THAT HEIGHT MADE BREATHING DIFFICULT.

CHOKE.. URGH!

TAKE IT EASY.. BREATHE SLOWLY. YOU'LL MAKE IT.

THE SNOW WAS POWDERY AND MADE THE CLIMB TREACHEROUS.

THE SOLDIERS HAD GOT NO TIME TO ACCLIMATISE THEMSELVES. WITH VIKRAM ENCOURAGING THEM, THEY CONTINUED UP.

SUDDENLY –

SWOOOOOOSH!!

GET DOWN! PLAY DEAD!

THE PAKISTANI ARMY WAS SCANNING THE AREA WITH FLARES TO DETECT MOVEMENT FROM THE INDIAN SIDE.

AFTER SOME TIME –

IT SEEMS SAFE NOW. LET'S MOVE.

*LOW ON OXYGEN

THE FLARES WERE NOT THE END OF THEIR PROBLEMS. AS THEY MADE THEIR WAY UP –

ZING!

DAG DAG DAG!

THEY ARE FIRING! TAKE COVER AND LIE LOW.

THE PAKISTANI SOLDIERS WERE TAKING EVERY PRECAUTION. BUT THEY DID NOT KNOW WHAT THE INDIAN ARMY WAS PLANNING, AND THEY WERE GETTING WEARY.

THE RADIO CRACKLED –

GO BACK, SHERSHAH! WE'LL KILL YOU IF YOU COME HERE*.

THE PAKISTANIS SENSED AN ATTACK BUT COULD NOT FIGURE OUT THE DIRECTION.

RUN WHILE YOU CAN, BECAUSE WE ARE COMING FOR YOU!

THE TROOPS FINALLY REACHED THE TOP.

GOOD, THEY STILL EXPECT US FROM THE FRONT! WE HAVE TO CLEAR THE FIVE BUNKERS THERE. CAPT. JAMWAL AND HIS MEN WILL CLEAR THE TWO ON THE TOP.

*IT WAS NORMAL FOR THE ENEMY TO INTERCEPT RADIO COMMUNICATIONS.

MEANWHILE BATRA AND HIS MEN CHARGED TOWARDS THE LOWER BUNKERS.

FOR INDIA!

SOME OF THE PAKISTANI SOLDIERS, IN THEIR PANIC TO GET TO SAFETY, TUMBLED DOWN THE CLIFF!

THERE WAS NO STOPPING THE INDIAN SIDE. THEY TORE THROUGH THE PAKISTANI DEFENCES.

SOON –

YEH DIL MAANGE MORE!

THE BASE ERUPTED IN JOY AS VIKRAM'S VOICE RESOUNDED THROUGH THE RADIO!

THE TRICOLOUR FLEW OVER POINT 5140!

THE MISSION TO CAPTURE THE POINT WAS A SUCCESS. THE INDIAN SIDE DID NOT LOSE A SINGLE SOLDIER.

SOON AFTER –

VIKRAM, WE NEED DELTA COMPANY TO CLEAR A POINT IN THE MUSHKOH VALLEY.

THERE IS HEAVY FIRING FROM THREE MACHINE GUNS FROM A LEDGE NORTH OF POINT 4875. IT IS MAKING THINGS DIFFICULT FOR THE MEN THERE. WE NEED THAT RIDGE CLEARED.

ON 4 JULY, 1999, DELTA COMPANY BEGAN ANOTHER CLIMB. THOUGH VIKRAM WAS RUNNING A FEVER, HE INSISTED ON GOING WITH HIS MEN.

I KNOW THE CLIMB IS DIFFICULT AND WE ARE ALL TIRED BUT WE CAN DO THIS!

ON THE MORNING OF 7 JULY –

IT'S TAKEN US LONGER TO REACH THAN WE HAD PLANNED. WE'LL HAVE TO BE MORE CAREFUL. FOLLOW ME.

MUST GET THIS RIGHT...

VIKRAM HAD DESTROYED THE FIRST MACHINE GUN SINGLE-HANDEDLY.

...AND DESTROYED THE FIRST TWO BUNKERS.

BUT IN THE SKIRMISH, VIKRAM HAD TAKEN A HIT.

SA'AB, YOU'RE HURT.

THERE IS NO TIME TO LOOK AT IT NOW. WE HAVE TO CLEAR THE AREA FIRST.

THE THREE MACHINE GUNS HAVE BEEN DESTROYED. THE ENEMY IS RETREATING.

BUT THERE IS STILL SOME SHOOTING COMING FROM THAT END. WE NEED TO DEAL WITH THAT TOO.

SUDDENLY —

AAAARGH!

EVERYONE WATCHED IN HORROR AS CAPT. VIKRAM BATRA FELL TO THE GROUND.

THEY COULD NOT BELIEVE THAT THEIR BELOVED SHERSHAH WAS DEAD.

THE ENTIRE GROUP OF SOLDIERS CHARGED FORWARD IN ANGER.

THE ENEMY FLED IN TERROR. THE ENTIRE CLIFF HAD BEEN CLEARED.

THE INDIAN ARMY WAS ABLE TO CAPTURE POINT 4875. IT WAS A HUGE VICTORY FOR THE INDIAN SIDE.

VIKRAM BATRA'S BODY WAS BROUGHT HOME WITH FULL MILITARY HONOURS.

GENERAL SALUTE – SALAAMI SHASTRA*.

MAYBE THERE IS A REASON GOD GAVE ME TWINS. ONE MARKED FOR THE COUNTRY AND THE OTHER FOR ME.

POINT 4875 WAS RENAMED CAPT. VIKRAM BATRA HILL. THE BRAVE SOLDIER WAS AWARDED THE PARAM VIR CHAKRA FOR HIS LIONHEARTED LEADERSHIP AND SELFLESS ACTIONS DURING THE KARGIL WAR.

*AS A MARK OF RESPECT TO THE MARTYR, SOLDIERS GIVE AN ARMED SALUTE WITH THEIR RIFLES UPRIGHT, FACING FRONT. THIS IS FOLLOWED BY A 21 GUN SALUTE BY A FIRING PARTY.

Weapons and Vehicles

Gnat: The Folland Gnat was the last plane made by British aircraft designer WEW Petter. This subsonic light fighter aircraft, which was also used as a jet trainer, was characterised by its small size, angled wings and simple design. It carried a crew of one pilot, two 30mm ADEN cannons, two bombs and 18 three-inch rockets. It had a range of 800km and a maximum speed of 1120kmph at 20,000ft.

The Gnat was inducted into the Indian Air Force in 1958, and was widely used. Later, the IAF began to manufacture it under license. Eventually, the design was improved and the modifications resulted in HAL Ajeet.

Bren Guns/Light Machine Guns: Automatic handheld guns that are designed to be fired by a single soldier without assistance. They typically use smaller caliber cartridges, but have heavier barrels than rifles.

Medium Machine Guns: An automatic firearm that uses cartridges fed by an ammunition belt. They are designed to be fired from a stationary position. It is portable, but typically needs more than one person to carry.

Rifles with bayonets: Firearms that shoot bullets with great precision because of the grooves cut in the inner surface of the barrel. Bayonets are dagger-like weapons that can be attached to the muzzle of a rifle to be used in hand-to-hand combat.

Recoilless Guns: Lightweight tube artillery that, at the moment of ignition, expels a large amount of the propellant gases that creates a forward push to counter the gun's backward momentum when fired. This way, the gun can launch a powerful projectile, without getting the heavy recoil of a cannon.

Rocket Launcher: Artillery device used to launch a projectile propelled by a rocket. There are smaller ones that can be carried on the shoulder, while larger ones can be mounted on jeeps.

Khukri: A specialised knife with a curved broad blade. The khukri is the characteristic weapon of the Gorkha regiments.

Spitfires: British single-seater fighter aircraft that the Indian Air Force began using in October 1944. These are short-range and high performance aircraft that were designed, and commonly used to prevent bombers and enemy recon aircraft from completing their missions.

Anti-tank jeeps: Jeeps that come equipped with weapon systems designed to hit and destroy heavily armoured vehicles, especially tanks.

Armoured cars: Combat vehicles that are protected by strong armour and bulletproof glass, enabling them to withstand shrapnel, bullets or shells from enemy fire. These vehicles are heavily equipped with weapons, making them both offensive and defensive mobile units used to carry troops into battle.

Surface to Air missiles: Missiles launched from the ground, designed to take down aircraft

Mine detectors: A handheld device used for locating buried or concealed anti-tank mines. They typically work by identifying the presence of metal in the ground.

Centurion tanks: Developed and manufactured in Great Britain, Centurion tanks began being used in 1945. They were heavily armed main battle tanks that weighed 51,820kg. One tank could carry a crew of four, and moved at a speed of 34kmph.
Centurion tanks were used in India during the 1965 war with Pakistan. All the tanks were assigned names, by which they were referred to during the war. Second Lieutenant Arun Khetarpal's tank was a Centurion tank named Famagusta.

Second Lieutenant Arun Khetarpal's tank, Famagusta, restored and kept in display by the Indian Army

In Times of Peace

What do the Armed Forces do in peace time? Is there a role for them when there is no war?

The primary role of the Armed Forces is to defend the nation against external aggression. Success in war comes to those who are well equipped and trained. The Armed Forces, therefore, constantly train themselves so that they are better prepared than the adversary for any eventuality.

India has very long borders which mostly do not follow geographic features. Most of our borders are active and conflict prone due to difference in perception with our neighbours. In order to guard these active borders, especially in mountainous and inhospitable terrain, the Army remains deployed to thwart recurring encroachment attempts and to battle relentless ceasefire violations. The Air Force and the Navy remain in a state of readiness to respond to any impending air or sea threats to our country.

Armed Forces units and formations, stationed in peace locations, follow a rigorous training routine which include physical and weapon training, arms/equipment repair and maintenance tasks, in order to remain operationally ready. Regular two-sided exercises and war games in which various defensive and offensive scenarios are enacted, are undertaken to validate and update operational plans and battle procedures. Logistic planning and preparation for operations and contingencies are also undertaken.

The Armed Forces are called upon to assist in times of internal disorders and calamities both natural and man-made such as floods, earthquakes etc. On 26 December, 2004, when a devastating tsunami swept across the Indian Ocean submerging islands, destroying coastlines and taking thousands of lives, the Air Force and the Navy swung into action carrying out rescue missions and transporting medical and food supplies to the Andaman & Nicobar Islands, Sri Lanka and the Maldives. More recently the floods in Jammu & Kashmir saw men from the Armed Forces deployed in rescuing hundreds of people from the fury of the rising water.

The Armed Forces are also called upon to restore peace and order during internal strife and unrest. The Indian Navy by patrolling the waters, guards the international shipping corridors in the Indian Ocean against the threat of piracy and terrorism.

Apart from securing the nation against external and internal threats, the Indian Army has been involved in nation building initiatives too through multifaceted activities such as laying bridges, providing medical facilities, running educational and vocational training, etc., for common people especially in inaccessible areas of J&K and the north-eastern states.

When mandated, the Armed Forces also participate in conflict prevention in neighbouring countries as during Operation Pawan in Sri Lanka (1987) and Operation Cactus in the Maldives (1988).

The Armed Forces also participate in peace-keeping missions of the United Nations under the UN Flag.

PVC Awardees

Major Somnath Sharma
1922-1947
Indo-Pak War (1947-48)

Lance Naik Karam Singh
1915-1993
Indo-Pak War (1947-48)

Second Lieutenant Rama Raghoba Rane
1918-1994
Indo-Pak War (1947-48)

Naik Yadunath Singh
1916-1948
Indo-Pak War (1947-48)

Company Havildar Major Piru Singh Shekhawat
1918-1948
Indo-Pak War (1947-48)

Captain Gurbachan Singh Salaria
1935-1961
Congo Crisis (1960-65)

Major Dhan Singh Thapa
1928-2005
Sino-Indian War (1962)

Subedar Joginder Singh
1921-1962
Sino-Indian War (1962)

Major Shaitan Singh
1924-1962
Sino-Indian War (1962)

Company Quarter Master Havildar Abdul Hamid
1933-1965
Indo-Pak War (1965)

Lieutenant-Colonel Ardeshir Burzorji . Tarapore
1923-1965
Indo-Pak War (1965)

Lance Naik Albert Ekka
1942-1971
Bangladesh Liberation War (1971)

Flying Officer Nirmaljit Singh Sekhon
1943-1971
Bangladesh Liberation War (1971)

Second Lieutenant Arun Khetarpal
1950-1971
Bangladesh Liberation War (1971)

Major Hoshiar Singh
1937-1998
Bangladesh Liberation War (1971)

Naib Subedar Bana Singh
Born 1949
Siachen Conflict

Major Ramaswamy Parameswaran
1946-1987
Operation Pawan (1987)

Captain Manoj Kumar Pandey
1975-1999
Kargil War (1999)

Grenadier Yogendra Singh Yadav
Born 1980
Kargil War (1999)

Rifleman Sanjay Kumar
Born 1976
Kargil War (1999)

Captain Vikram Batra
1974-1999
Kargil War (1999)

Amar Chitra Katha's

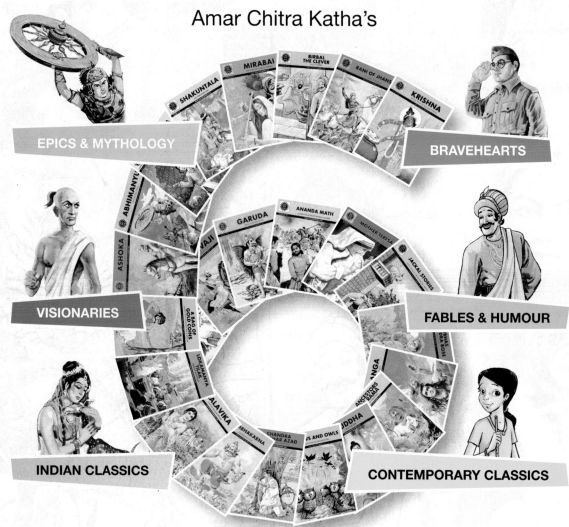

EPICS & MYTHOLOGY

BRAVEHEARTS

VISIONARIES

FABLES & HUMOUR

INDIAN CLASSICS

CONTEMPORARY CLASSICS

EXCITING STORY CATEGORIES, ONE AMAZING DESTINATION.

From the episodes of Mahabharata to the wit of Birbal,
from the valour of Shivaji to the teachings of Tagore,
from the adventures of Pratapan to the tales of Ruskin Bond –
Amar Chitra Katha stories span across different genres to get you the best of literature.